Lectures on Symmetries

Documents on Modern Physics

Edited by

ELLIOT W. MONTROLL, *University of Rochester*
GEORGE H. VINEYARD, *Brookhaven National Laboratory*
MAURICE LÉVY, *Université de Paris*

A. ABRAGAM L'Effet Mössbauer
S. T. BELYAEV Collective Excitations in Nuclei
P. G. BERGMANN and A. YASPAN Physics of Sound in the Sea: Part I Transmission
T. A. BRODY Symbol-manipulation Techniques for Physics
K. G. BUDDEN Lectures on Magnetoionic Theory
J. W. CHAMBERLAIN Motion of Charged Particles in the Earth's Magnetic Field
S. CHAPMAN Solar Plasma, Geomagnetism, and Aurora
H.-Y. CHIU Neutrino Astrophysics
A. H. COTTRELL Theory of Crystal Dislocations
J. DANON Lectures on the Mössbauer Effect
B. S. DEWITT Dynamical Theory of Groups and Fields
R. H. DICKE The Theoretical Significance of Experimental Relativity
P. FONG Statistical Theory of Nuclear Fission
E. GERJUOY, A. YASPAN and J. K. MAJOR Physics of Sound in the Sea: Parts II and III Reverberation, and Reflection of Sound from Submarines and Surface Vessels
M. GOURDIN Lagrangian Formalism and Symmetry Laws
D. HESTENES Space–Time Algebra
J. G. KIRKWOOD Dielectrics — Intermolecular Forces — Optical Rotation
J. G. KIRKWOOD Macromolecules
J. G. KIRKWOOD Proteins
J. G. KIRKWOOD Quantum Statistics and Cooperative Phenomena
J. G. KIRKWOOD Selected Topics in Statistical Mechanics
J. G. KIRKWOOD Shock and Detonation Waves
J. G. KIRKWOOD Theory of Liquids
J. G. KIRKWOOD Theory of Solutions
V. KOURGANOFF Introduction to the General Theory of Particle Transfer

R. LATTÈS Methods of Resolution for Selected Boundary Problems in Mathematical Physics

J. LEQUEUX Structure and Evolution of Galaxies

J. L. LOPES Lectures on Symmetries

F. E. LOW Symmetries and Elementary Particles

P. H. E. MEIJER Quantum Statistical Mechanics

M. MOSHINSKY Group Theory and the Many-body Problem

M. MOSHINSKY The Harmonic Oscillator in Modern Physics: From Atoms to Quarks

M. NIKOLIĆ Analysis of Scattering and Decay

M. NIKOLIĆ Kinematics and Multiparticle Systems

A. B. PIPPARD The Dynamics of Conduction Electrons

H. REEVES Stellar Evolution and Nucleosynthesis

L. SCHWARTZ Application of Distributions to the Theory of Elemetary Particles in Quantum Mechanics

J. SCHWINGER Particles and Sources

J. SCHWINGER and D. S. SAXON Discontinuities in Waveguides

M. TINKHAM Superconductivity

R. WILDT Physics of Sound in the Sea: Part IV Acoustic Properties of Wakes

LECTURES ON SYMMETRIES

J. LEITE LOPES
Centro Brasileiro de Pesquisas Físicas
Rio de Janeiro
and
Carnegie-Mellon University
Pittsburgh, Pennsylvania

GORDON AND BREACH Science Publishers
New York London Paris

150 Fifth Avenue, New York, N. Y. 10011
Library of Congress catalog card number: 70-99105

Editorial office for the United Kingdom:
Gordon and Breach, Science Publishers Ltd.
12 Bloomsbury Way
London W. C. 1

Editorial office for France:
Gordon & Breach
7-9 rue Emile Dubois
Paris 14^e^

Printed in east Germany.

Contents

Part One

CLASSICAL SYMMETRIES: AN ELEMENTARY SURVEY

CHAPTER 1

Symmetries in Classical Mechanics of Systems of Point-Particles

1.1 THE LAGRANGE AND CANONICAL EQUATIONS

The kinetic energy of a classical system of n point-particles, A, is:

$$T = \sum_{A=1}^{n} \tfrac{1}{2} m_A (\dot{\mathbf{x}}_A)^2 \tag{1.1}$$

where m_A is the mass of particle A at position $\mathbf{x}_A$ and the dot over a letter denotes, as usual, its time derivative. Let V be the potential energy of this system, a function which, in general, depends on the position of each particle and on time—it may also depend on the particles' velocities, which is the case of the so-called velocity-dependent potentials.

The Lagrangian is then defined as the difference between T and V:

$$L = T - V \tag{1.2}$$

and is clearly a function of each particle's position, velocity and the time t:

$$L = L(\mathbf{x}_1, \ldots \mathbf{x}_n; \dot{\mathbf{x}}_1, \ldots \dot{\mathbf{x}}_n; t). \tag{1.3}$$

The existence of such a function, independently of the special definition (1.2), will be assumed for the dynamical systems we study in classical mechanics with the objective of a later transposition or generalisation into quantum mechanics and quantum field theory.

The action S between any two instants t_1 and t_2 is the time-integral of the Lagrangian:

$$S = \int_{t_1}^{t_2} L\, dt. \tag{1.4}$$

It depends not only on the two times t_1 and t_2 but also on the form of the function L: S is an ordinary function of t_1 and t_2 and a functional of L (this means that, for t_1 and t_2 fixed, to each function L there corresponds a numerical value for S):

$$S = S[L; t_1, t_2] \tag{1.5}$$

Between the instants t_1 and t_2 there exists, *a priori*, an infinite set Γ of possible trajectories for the dynamical system; out of these, *the system describes, in fact, that trajectory which makes S stationary*, i.e., gives a minimum or maximum. This is Hamilton's principle or the postulate of minimal action or simply the action principle.

Let α denote a parameter designed to distinguish, for a given time t, the positions of each particle A in each of the possible trajectories of the set Γ:

$$\mathbf{x}_A = \mathbf{x}_A(t; \alpha) \tag{1.6}$$

As the integration in (1.4) is over t, the functional S in (1.5) will also depend on α:

$$S = S[L; t_1, t_2; \alpha] \tag{1.5a}$$

Let a given value of α, $\alpha = 0$ say, correspond to that trajectory which makes S stationary and define the variation of x_{jA} as:

$$\delta x_{jA} = \left(\frac{\partial x_{jA}}{\partial \alpha}\right)_{\alpha=0} d\alpha, \quad j = 1, 2, 3; \quad A = 1, 2, \dots n$$

The action principle is expressed by the requirement:

$$\delta S = 0 \tag{1.7}$$

For t_1 and t_2 fixed, one has:

$$\delta S = \int_{t_1}^{t_2} \delta L \, dt \tag{1.8}$$

with (see Fig. 1)

$$\delta x_{jA}(t_1) = \delta x_{jA}(t_2) = 0 \tag{1.8a}$$

and hence, according to (1.3) and (1.8)

$$\delta S = \int_{t_1}^{t_2} \sum_{A=1}^{n} \sum_{j=1}^{3} \left\{ \frac{\partial L}{\partial x_{jA}} \delta x_{jA} + \frac{\partial L}{\partial \dot{x}_{jA}} \delta \dot{x}_{jA} \right\} dt. \tag{1.8b}$$

The interchange of the symbols δ and d/dt, and the identity:

$$\frac{\partial L}{\partial \dot{x}_{jA}} \frac{d}{dt} \delta x_{jA} = \frac{d}{dt}\left(\frac{\partial L}{\partial \dot{x}_{jA}} \delta x_{jA}\right) - \delta x_{jA}\left(\frac{d}{dt} \frac{\partial L}{\partial \dot{x}_{jA}}\right)$$

lead us to write (1.8b) in the following form:

$$\delta S = \int_{t_1}^{t_2} \sum_{A=1}^{n} \sum_{j=1}^{3} \left\{ \left[\frac{\partial L}{\partial x_{jA}} - \left(\frac{d}{dt} \frac{\partial L}{\partial \dot{x}_{jA}} \right) \right] \delta x_{jA} + \frac{d}{dt} \left(\frac{\partial L}{\partial \dot{x}_{jA}} \delta x_{jA} \right) \right\} dt.$$

A partial integration and the conditions (1.8a) make the last term of the above form of δS to vanish.

We are thus left with:

$$\delta S = \int_{t_1}^{t_2} \sum_A \sum_j \left\{ \frac{\partial L}{\partial x_{jA}} - \frac{d}{dt} \left(\frac{\partial L}{\partial \dot{x}_{jA}} \right) \right\} \delta x_{jA}\, dt.$$

The postulate (1.7), valid for arbitrary variations δx_{jA}, thus leads to the well known Lagrange equations:

$$\frac{\partial L}{\partial x_{jA}} - \frac{d}{dt} \frac{\partial L}{\partial \dot{x}_{jA}} = 0, \quad j = 1, 2, 3; \quad A = 1, \ldots, n. \qquad (1.9)$$

The knowledge of the equations of motion of our system of particles is, in this way, connected with that of the Lagrangian.

To these equations of motion one must add the initial conditions in order to determine the orbit of the mechanical system. In classical mechanics, the *observables* are the positions and velocities of particles. The values of the $6n$ quantities $x_{jA}(t_0)$, $\dot{x}_{jA}(t_0)$, at a given instant t_0—the results of the observations (for measurements) of these variables at this instant—may provide a set of such conditions.

The momentum of particle A, canonically conjugate to its coordinate x_{jA}, is defined by the relation:

$$p_{jA} = \frac{\partial L}{\partial \dot{x}_{jA}}, \quad j = 1, 2, 3; \quad A = 1, \ldots, n. \qquad (1.10)$$

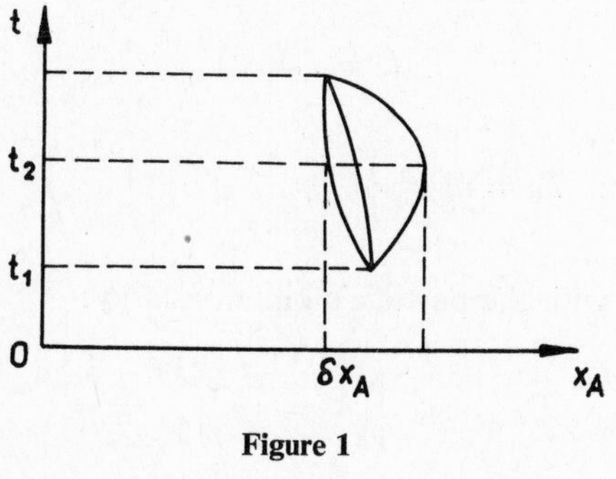

Figure 1

If these equations are solved so that one may express the velocities $\dot{x}$ in terms of the momenta, the Hamiltonian of the system, as defined by:

$$H = \sum_{j,A} p_{jA}\dot{x}_{jA} - L \tag{1.11}$$

will be the function of the independent variables x_{jA}, p_{jA} and t:

$$H = H(\mathbf{x}_1, \mathbf{p}_1, \ldots, \mathbf{x}_n, \mathbf{p}_n; t) \tag{1.11a}$$

The equations (1.9), (1.10) and (1.11) give the well-known canonical equations:

$$\dot{x}_{jA} = \frac{\partial H}{\partial p_{jA}}, \quad \dot{p}_{jA} = -\frac{\partial H}{\partial x_{jA}} \tag{1.12}$$

a system of $6n$ differential equations of first-order, equivalent to the second-order $3n$ equations (1.9).

A typical illustration of the fact that the definition (1.2) is not always valid, is provided by a particle, the velocity of which is not small if compared to the velocity of light c; although the notion of potential energy $V(\mathbf{x})$ is still assumed to be valid, a mass variation with the velocity is required by relativity theory:

$$m = \beta m_0 \quad \beta = \left(1 - \frac{v^2}{c^2}\right)^{-1/2}. \tag{1.13}$$

And the equation of motion:

$$\frac{dp_j}{dt} = -\frac{\partial V}{\partial x_j}$$

with

$$p_j = mv_j = m\dot{x}_j$$

is deduced from a Lagrangian:

$$L = T_0 - V$$

where

$$T_0 = m_0c^2\left\{1 - \left(1 - \frac{\mathbf{v}^2}{c^2}\right)^{-1/2}\right\}$$

does not coincide with the particle's kinetic energy:

$$T = m_0c^2\left\{\left(1 - \frac{\mathbf{v}^2}{c^2}\right)^{-1/2} - 1\right\} \tag{1.14}$$

1.2 CONSERVATION OF MECHANICAL ENERGY

In general, therefore, the Hamiltonian is a function of the particles' positions, momenta and time, as stated in formula (1.11a). Its total rate of change with time is thus:

$$\frac{dH}{dt} = \frac{\partial H}{\partial t} + \sum_{j,A} \left(\frac{\partial H}{\partial x_{jA}} \frac{dx_{jA}}{dt} + \frac{\partial H}{\partial p_{jA}} \frac{dp_{jA}}{dt} \right).$$

Each term of the summation on the right-hand side vanishes in virtue of (1.12):

$$\frac{dH}{dt} = \frac{\partial H}{\partial t}.$$

It is concluded that if the Hamiltonian does not depend on t in an explicit fashion (it depends implicitly on time through $x_{jA}(t)$ and $p_{jA}(t)$), its total rate of change with time vanishes:

$$\frac{dH}{dt} = 0.$$

The Hamiltonian will then be equal to a constant E, conserved in time, the energy of the mechanical system:

$$H(\mathbf{x}_1 . \mathbf{p}_1, \ldots, \mathbf{x}_n, \mathbf{p}_n) = E.$$

1.3 POISSON BRACKETS AND CONSTANTS OF MOTION

Let $F(\mathbf{x}_1, \mathbf{p}_1, \ldots, \mathbf{x}_n, \mathbf{p}_n; t)$ and $G(\mathbf{x}_1, \mathbf{p}_1, \ldots_n, \mathbf{p}_n; t)$ be two dynamical variables of our system of particles—functions of time and of the particles' coordinates and momenta. An important quantity associated with this system is defined by means of such a pair of dynamical variables. It is the Poisson bracket of F and G, expressed as:

$$\{F, G\} = \sum_{j,A} \left(\frac{\partial F}{\partial x_{jA}} \frac{\partial G}{\partial p_{jA}} - \frac{\partial F}{\partial p_{jA}} \frac{\partial G}{\partial x_{jA}} \right). \tag{1.15}$$

This function is adequate to a more elegant form of the equations of motion, and allows a simple proof of fundamental theorems on symmetries and constants of motion, as we shall see. Moreover, it is this form of the equations of motion which allows a straightforward transition from the classical to the quantum-mechanical description of physical systems (which have a classical limit).

The total rate of change of F with time is:

$$\frac{dF}{dt} = \frac{\partial F}{\partial t} + \sum_{j,A} \left(\frac{\partial F}{\partial x_{jA}} \frac{dx_{jA}}{dt} + \frac{\partial F}{\partial p_{jA}} \frac{dp_{jA}}{dt} \right)$$

which, in view of the canonical equations (1.12) and the definition (1.15), takes the form:

$$\frac{dF}{dt} = \frac{\partial F}{\partial t} + \{F, H\}. \tag{1.16}$$

In particular, the canonical equations read:

$$\dot{x}_{jA} = \{x_{jA}, H\}, \qquad \dot{p}_{jA} = \{p_{jA}, H\} \tag{1.17}$$

and the fundamental Poisson brackets, relative to the particles' coordinates and momenta, are:

$$\begin{aligned} \{x_{jA}, x_{kB}\} &= \{p_{jA}, p_{kB}\} = 0 \\ \{x_{jA}, p_{kB}\} &= \delta_{jk}\delta_{AB} \end{aligned} \tag{1.18}$$

with $j, k = 1, 2, 3$; $A, B = 1, 2, \ldots, n$.

A dynamical variable F is a *constant of motion* if its total rate of change with time vanishes:

$$\frac{dF}{dt} = 0\,.$$

According to equation (1.16), this will be the case *if F does not depend explicitly on time and its Poisson bracket with the Hamiltonian is equal to zero.*

1.4 SYMMETRIES AND INVARIANCE PRINCIPLES

The notion of symmetry—in sculpture, painting and architecture, in the crystalline and biological forms, in mathematics, in physics—has been masterfully discussed in a beautiful booklet by Herman Weyl. "If I am not mistaken, writes Weyl, the word symmetry is used in our everyday language in two meanings. In the one sense symmetric means something like well-proportioned, well-balanced, and symmetry denotes that sort of concordance of several parts by which they integrate into a whole. *Beauty* is bound up with symmetry (...). The image of the balance provides a natural link to the second sense in which the word symmetry is used in modern times: *bilateral symmetry*, the symmetry of left and right, which is so conspicuous in the structure of the higher animals, especially the human body. Now this bilateral symmetry is a strictly geometric and, in contrast to the vague notion of symmetry discussed before, an absolute precise concept. A body, a spatial configuration, is symmetric to a given plane E if it is carried into itself by reflection in E (...). A mapping is defined whenever a rule is established by which every point p (of a spatial configuration) is associated with an image p'. Another example: a rotation around a perpendicular axis (to a plane), say by 30°, carries each point p of space into a point p' and thus defines a mapping. A figure has rotational symmetry around an axis l if it is carried into itself by all rotations around l" [(1)*].

One is thus led to consider special sets of mappings, of one-to-one transformations of a given space into itself, with respect to which the laws of a theory are invariant. These special sets are the so-called groups; a set S of transformations $T_1, T_2, \ldots$ is a group if, given any two elements of this set, T_i, T_j, one can define a product (or composition) $T_k = T_i T_j$ such that:

a) T_k belongs to the set S;

b) the identity I is an element of S and is such that for any $T_j : T_j I = IT_j = T_j$;

c) to each element T_j of S there is associated an inverse, T_j^{-1}, belonging to S, and defined by the equality

$$T_j^{-1} T_j = T_j T_j^{-1} = I.$$

The symmetries of a spatial configuration, of a physical system, of a set of laws of nature, are thus defined by those groups of transformations which leave invariant the given configuration, physical system, or natural laws—and they are thus appropriately called the corresponding *symmetry groups.*

Of course, the search for such symmetries, for the invariance properties of the laws of nature is meaningful; although they do not change the forms of these laws, they have observable consequences because the initial conditions

* References are listed on page 85.

associated to the laws of nature are not unchanged under the transformations of the group.

According to Houtappel, Van Dam and Wigner,[2] one can distinguish two types of definition of an invariance principle. To the adepts of the first definition, the generally valid invariance principles are only those which *postulate the equivalence of the frames of reference which can physically be changed into each other*. As a frame of reference consists of an observer equipped with all necessary measuring devices, this definition restricts the invariance transformations to space and time translations, to rotations and, more generally, to inhomogeneous Lorentz transformations.

The second definition of an invariance principle *postulates as generally valid all those* (simple) *transformations which leave the laws of nature invariant, independently of whether one can or cannot physically change one observer and his apparatus into another* by such transformations. The operation of time reversal or the transformation *CPT* which consists of the product of time reversal, space reflection and charge conjugation are examples of such transformations which cannot physically carry an observer into another.

It is within the context of the first definition—that of physically equivalent reference frames—that one may distinguish, following Wigner, two equivalent points of view for carrying an invariance transformation. The *active* transformations change the object; the observer in his reference frame investigates the correlation between his measurements on the object before and after the transformation. According to the *passive* viewpoint, the transformations are correlations between the observations made by two different observers on the same object (Fig.2). It is the passive type of geometric and kinematic transformations which is usually considered in classical physics, mainly, after the fundamental papers and booklets by Einstein on the special theory of relativity. Clearly, in the example pictured in Fig.2, one can always, given the active transformation $AB \Rightarrow AB'$ for the observer S, imagine a second observer, S' who is in the same relation to the observations made on AB' as the first observer S is to his measurements on the original system AB.

It must, however, be mentioned that the second definition of invariance principle—which regards as valid all those simple transformations which keep the laws of nature invariant—is more general and allowed the discovery of non-geometrical (or dynamical) symmetries of certain interactions, such as the isospin, and more generally, the unitary spin symmetry of strong interactions in elementary particle physics. The gauge transformations, associated to the definition of current and charge conservation, are also non-geometrical.

(a) Active transformation:

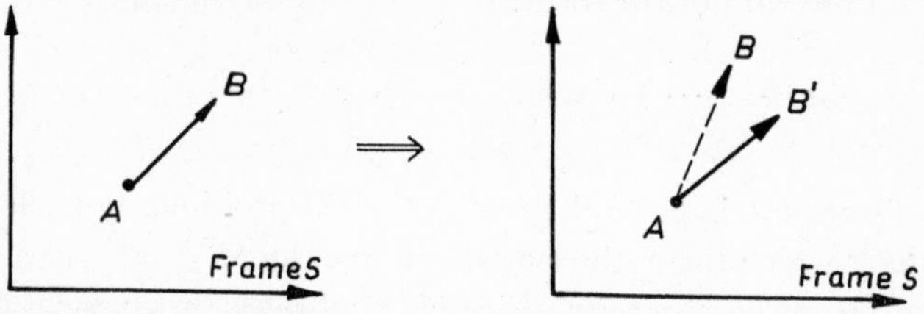

(b) Passive transformation:

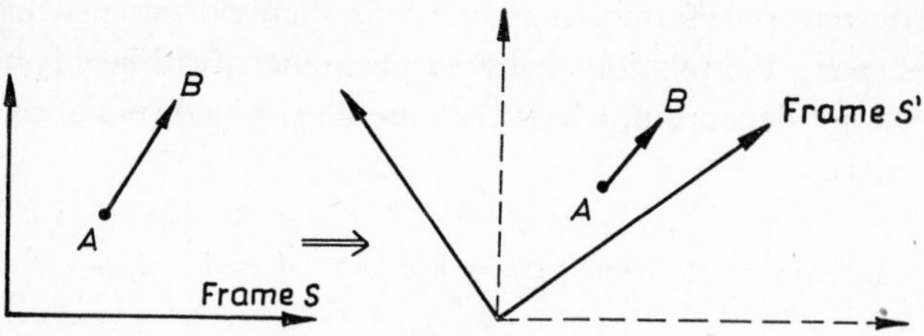

Figure 2

1.5. SYMMETRIES AND THE STRUCTURE OF PHYSICAL SPACE IN CLASSICAL MECHANICS

The equations of a classical system of point-particles are invariant under certain transformations of reference frames. The invariance under each specific group of transformations results from a basic principle, of empirical origin.

1.5.1. First of all, there is the *principle of absolute time in Newtonian* mechanics. It states that the time interval between two mechanical events, as measured in a reference frame, is independent of the state of motion of the frame. The principle is not generally true—it holds only for velocities which are small compared to the light velocity c. Newton, however, believed in an "absolute, true and mathematical time of itself, and from its own nature, (which) flows equably, without relation to anything external, and by another name is called duration". He, therefore, assumed that the clocks of all observers, whatever their state of relative motion, could be synchronised by means of signals, which would have to propagate with infinite speed. Newtonian mechanics is a theory of action at a distance. Actually, all known physical interactions propagate with a finite velocity and Einstein's theory of relativity allows one to show that this maximum velocity is equal to c.

1.5.2. The equations of motion of an isolated system of n point-particles, in an inertial frame, are of the form:

$$m_A \ddot{x}_{jA} = \sum_{B \neq A} F_{jB}(\mathbf{x}_1 \ldots, \mathbf{x}_n, \dot{\mathbf{x}}_1, \ldots, \dot{\mathbf{x}}_n; t), \quad j = 1, 2, 3; \quad A, B = 1, 2, \ldots, n \tag{1.19}$$

where the forces are, in general, functions of the positions and velocities and of the time at which these observables are measured.

The principle of homogeneity of the physical space, in classical mechanics states that the equations (1.19) are invariant with respect to a change of the origin of the reference frame. In other words, there exist no privileged points in physical space, the relations between phenomena within this mechanical system must not depend on where they are determined (the absolute origin does not exist).

Let:

$$x'_{jA} = x_{jA} - a_j, \quad j = 1, 2, 3; \quad A = 1, \ldots, n \tag{1.20}$$

be the coordinates of our particles in the new reference frame, displaced by the constant vector **a** from the original one. It is seen that the displacement *invariance requires that the force depend only on the mutual distances between the point-particles*:

$$m_A \ddot{x}_{jA} = F_{jA} = \sum_{B \neq A} F_{jBA}(\mathbf{x}_{BA}, \dot{\mathbf{x}}_{BA}; t), \tag{1.19a}$$

$$x_{BA} = x_B - x_A.$$

The transformations (1.20) form the *group of translations* $T(\mathbf{a})$, depending on the three parameters a_j: the product of two translations $T(\mathbf{a})$ and $T(\mathbf{b})$ is a translation by $\mathbf{a} + \mathbf{b}$: $T(\mathbf{a})\,T(\mathbf{b}) = T(\mathbf{a} + \mathbf{b})$; the identity is $T(0)$ and the inverse of $T(\mathbf{a})$ is $T(-\mathbf{a})$.

1.5.3. The *principle of isotropy of the physical space* states that the equations of motion (1.19) are invariant with respect to any rotation of the reference frame. In other words, there are no privileged directions in space, the relations between events within our system of point-particles do not depend on the orientation of the whole system in space.

A rotation around the origin of the Cartesian coordinates system associated to reference frame S, with basis $|e_1)$, $|e_2)$, $|e_0)$, changes all vectors:

$$|x_A) = \sum_{j=1}^{3} x_{jA} |e_j), \qquad A = 1, \ldots, n \tag{1.21}$$

into new vectors:

$$|x'_A) = \sum_{j=1}^{3} x_{jA}|e'_j) \tag{1.22}$$

where $|e'_1)$, $|e'_2)$, $|e'_3)$ are the basis-vectors of the new coordinate system S'.

Expressed in terms of the basis of the original system S, the new vectors $|x'_A)$ will have new coordinates x'_{jA}:

$$|x'_A) = \sum_j x'_{jA}|e_j). \tag{1.23}$$

In correspondence with the vector space Σ spanned by all linear combinations (1.21), one defines a *dual space*, a vector of which will be denoted by the symbol $(x|$. The space Σ will have Euclidian structure if, to each vector $|b)$ of R and $(a|$ of its dual, one associates a number denoted by $(a|b)$, the scalar product of the two vectors, with the properties:

1) $(a|a) \geqq 0$ and $(a|a) = 0$ implies $|a) = |0)$ where $|0)$ is the null vector;

2) $(a|b) = (b|a)^*$, where in general Σ comprises vectors with complex numbers as coordinates;

3) α being a complex number one must have $(a|\alpha b) = \alpha\,(a|b)$;

4) $((a_1 + a_2)|b) = (a_1|b) + (a_2|b)$.

If the two given coordinate systems S and S' are Cartesian, their bases will be orthonormal, i.e.

$$(e_k|e_l) = (e'_k|e'_l) = \delta_{kl}, \qquad k, l = 1, 2, 3. \tag{1.24}$$

Therefore the comparison of equations (1.22) and (1.23) gives rise, in view of (1.24), to the well-known homogeneous linear relations between the coordinates x_{jA} and x'_{jA}:

$$x'_{jA} = \sum_k a_{jk} x_{kA} \tag{1.25}$$

corresponding to the given rotation. And this is determined by the 9 numbers a_{jk}:

$$a_{jk} = (e_j|e'_k)$$

the cosinus of the angle between the k-axis of the system S' with the j-axis of system S.

The length of a vector $|x)$ is the non-negative number $[(x|x)]^{1/2}$ where, in Cartesian coordinate systems:

$$(x|y) = \sum_j x_j^* y_j.$$

These homogeneous linear transformations (1.25) which conserve the length of all vectors or, more generally, the scalar product:

$$(x|y) = (x'|y') \tag{1.26}$$

are called *unitary* transformations. In the particular case of real vector spaces, these transformations are called *orthogonal*. The latter ones keep invariant the bilinear form:

$$\sum_j x'_{jA} y'_{jA} = \sum_j x_{jA} y_{jA}$$

whence

$$\sum_j a_{jk} a_{jl} = \delta_{kl}. \tag{1.27}$$

(For the unitary transformations one has $\Sigma\, a^*_{jk} a_{jl} = \delta_{kl}$.)

Let us represent the nine numbers a_{jk} by a matrix R

$$R = \begin{pmatrix} a_{11} a_{12} a_{13} \\ a_{21} a_{22} a_{23} \\ a_{31} a_{32} a_{33} \end{pmatrix}. \tag{1.28}$$

The vector $|x_A)$ which has coordinates x_{jA} in a basis of the coordinate frame S will be represented by the one column matrix:

$$|x_A) = \begin{pmatrix} x_{1A} \\ x_{2A} \\ x_{3A} \end{pmatrix}, \quad A = 1, \dots n$$

if one chooses the following representation for the basis:

$$|e_1) = \begin{pmatrix} 1 \\ 0 \\ 0 \end{pmatrix}; \quad |e_2) = \begin{pmatrix} 0 \\ 1 \\ 0 \end{pmatrix}; \quad |e_3) = \begin{pmatrix} 0 \\ 0 \\ 1 \end{pmatrix}$$

The rule of multiplication of two matrices,

$$(R_1 R_2)_{kl} = \sum_n (R_1)_{kn} (R_2)_{nl}$$

leads us to write the equations (1.25) under the form:

$$|x'_A) = R|x_A). \tag{1.29}$$

The reader will be able to prove the relationship:

$$\sum_j |e_j)\,(e_j| = 1. \tag{1.30}$$

It is clear from the representation above that in the case of a complex vector space the passage to its dual space is performed by the operation of transposition and complex conjugation. In a real vector space, the dual vectors are the transposed (column → line) of the given ones. The fact that, in this case, the coordinates of $|x)$ and $(x|$, in the same basis, are the same real numbers, is usually translated by stating that the space and its dual coincide.

The relations (1.27) and (1.28) allow us to write for the orthogonal matrices:

$$R^T R = R R^T = I \tag{1.31}$$

where R^T means the transposed of R and I is the unit matrix. For unitary matrices U one has (invariance of relations (1.26) and (1.30)):

$$U^\dagger U = U U^\dagger = I$$

where $U\dagger = (U^T)^*$, the hermitian conjugate of U, is obtained by transposition and complex conjugation of U. It follows from (1.26), (1.29) and (1.31) that:

$$(x'_A| = (x_A|\, R^T \tag{1.32}$$

As the determinant of a matrix is the same as that of its transposed, one concludes from (1.31):

$$\det(R) = \pm 1 . \tag{1.33}$$

When transformations R have determinant $+1$

$$\det(R) = +1$$

they constitute the so-called group of *proper rotations*—they can be continuously generated from the identity.

When $\det(R) = -1$, the transformations are called *improper*—they contain the spatial reflections I_S (with respect to the origin)

$$x'_k = -x_k, \qquad k = 1, 2, 3 .$$

An improper transformation can be expressed as the product of I_S and a rotation.

Clearly, the equations (1.19) are invariant with respect to the group of rotations if the forces transform like vectors:

$$F'_{jBA}(\mathbf{x}'_{BA}, \dot{\mathbf{x}}'_{BA}; t) = \sum_k a_{jk} F_{kBA}(\mathbf{x}_{BA}, \dot{\mathbf{x}}_{BA}; t). \tag{1.34}$$

1.5.4 *The principle of classical (Newtonian or Galilei) relativity* states that the mechanical laws of an isolated system of n point particles established in an inertial frame of reference, S, are the same for another frame S', in rectilinear and uniform motion with respect to S. In other words, it is impossible, by means of mechanical observations within the system of point-particles, to detect the rectilinear uniform motion of an inertial reference frame.

The transformations between the coordinates of a point-particle A as referred to such frames S and S' are:

$$x'_{jA} = x_{jA} - v_j t, \qquad j = 1, 2, 3; \quad A = 1, \ldots, n \tag{1.34a}$$

where v_j are the components of the constant velocity of S' with respect to S. They form a group which depends on the three parameters v_j, the homogeneous Galilei-group, $G(\mathbf{v})$.

It is clear that the equations of motion (1.19a) will be invariant if the forces F_{jA} are Galilei-covariant vector functions of the instantaneous mutual distances and velocities of the particles; these forces have the form[(2)]:

$$F_{jA} = \sum_{B} (x_{jBA} f_{BA} + \dot{x}_{jBA} g_{BA})$$
$$+ \sum_{BC} [(\mathbf{x}_{BA} \times \mathbf{x}_{CA})_j f_{BCA} + (\dot{\mathbf{x}}_{BA} \times \dot{\mathbf{x}}_{CA})\, g_{BCA} + (\mathbf{x}_{BA} \times \dot{\mathbf{x}}_{CA})\, h_{CBA}]$$

where the f's, g's and h are Galilei-invariant functions of the coordinates and velocities.

1.6 CANONICAL TRANSFORMATIONS AND THE HAMILTON–JACOBI EQUATION

The connection between symmetries and constants of motion or conservation laws does not follow from Newton's equations of motion, but rather from the Lagrange's form of these equations. This will be seen in section 1.9. Until then we need to review some needed concepts.

Hamilton's principle, (1.4), (1.7) can be written, in view of the equation (1.11):

$$\delta \int_{t_1}^{t_2} \left\{ \sum_{jA} p_{jA}\, dx_{jA} - H\, dt \right\} = 0 . \tag{1.35}$$

We now introduce a new reference frame, S', with respect to which the coordinates and momenta of our system of point-particles, x'_{jA}, p'_{jA}, will be functions of the analogous variables as measured in the old frame S:

$$\begin{aligned} x'_{jA} &= x'_{jA}(\mathbf{x}_1, \mathbf{p}_1, \dots, \mathbf{x}_n, \mathbf{p}_n; t) \\ p'_{jA} &= p'_{jA}(\mathbf{x}_1, \mathbf{p}_1, \dots, \mathbf{x}_n, \mathbf{p}_n; t) \end{aligned} \qquad j = 1, 2, 3; \quad A = 1, 2, \dots, n \qquad (1.36)$$

It will be assumed that the mapping functions (1.36) are continuous, differentiable and have a non-vanishing Jacobian:

$$\det \begin{pmatrix} \dfrac{\partial x'_{11}}{\partial x_{11}} \cdots \dfrac{\partial x'_{11}}{\partial p_{3n}} \\ \cdot \; \cdot \; \cdot \; \cdot \; \cdot \; \cdot \; \cdot \; \cdot \\ \dfrac{\partial p'_{3n}}{\partial x_{11}} \cdots \dfrac{\partial p'_{3n}}{\partial p_{3n}} \end{pmatrix} \neq 0 \qquad (1.36a)$$

so that there will exist an inverse mapping:

$$\begin{aligned} x_{jA} &= x_{jA}(\mathbf{x}'_1, \mathbf{p}'_1, \dots, \mathbf{x}'_n, \mathbf{p}'_n; t) \\ p_{jA} &= p_{jA}(\mathbf{x}'_1, \mathbf{p}'_1, \dots, \mathbf{x}'_n, \mathbf{p}'_n; t). \end{aligned} \qquad (1.36b)$$

The group of canonical (or contact) *transformations* is the group of mappings (1.36) (1.36a) which leave the laws of the mechanics of systems of point-particles, (1.9) or (1.12), invariant.

For simplicity, let us represent by $X = (x, p)$ a point of the $6n$-dimensional phase-space, the coordinates of which are x_{jA}, p_{jA} with $j = 1, 2, 3$; $A = 1, \dots, n$.

Let $F(X, t)$ be a dynamical variable, a function of the observables x, p measured at a given time. This function will be mapped into another one, $F'(X', t)$ by the canonical transformations (1.36); the latter will be symbolised by the application of the operator $\mathscr{C}$ of the corresponding group:

$$X' = \mathscr{C}X, \qquad X = \mathscr{C}^{-1}X'. \qquad (3.17)$$

The group of canonical transformations $\mathscr{C}$ defined in the phase-space induces a set of transformations T in the space of functions $F(X, t)$:

$$F'(X, t) = TF(X, t). \qquad (1.38)$$

The transformed functions of the transformed orbits, $F'(X', t)$ will be defined as those which have the same values which the original functions assume for the original orbits:

$$F'(X', t) = F(X, t). \qquad (1.39)$$

In this way one will be able to associate the product of two mappings $T_1 T_2$ in the space of functions F to the product $\mathscr{C}_1 \mathscr{C}_2$ in the phase-space. In fact, it follows from (1.37), (1.38), (1.39) that (omitting t):

$$T_2 F(X) = F'(X) = F(\mathscr{C}_2^{-1} X). \tag{1.40}$$

One then substitutes $\mathscr{C}_1^{-1} X$ for X; this will induce a transformation which reads, according to (1.39):

$$T_1 F'(X) = F(\mathscr{C}_1^{-1} X)$$

and hence, in view of (1.40):

$$T_1 T_2 F(X) = F(\mathscr{C}_2^{-1} \mathscr{C}_1^{-1} X) = F([\mathscr{C}_1 \mathscr{C}_2]^{-1} X). \tag{1.41}$$

The Lagrangean and the Hamiltonian, however, do not satisfy the relation (1.39) because the definition of canonical transformations requires the invariance of the variation of the functional (1.5a):

$$\delta S\,[L; t_1, t_2; \alpha] = \delta S\,[L'; t_1, t_2 : \alpha]$$

where $L'(x', \dot{x}', t)$ is the new Lagrangian. This is satisfied by requiring that the two functionals differ by an ordinary function of t_1 and t_2:

$$S\,[L; t_1, t_2; \alpha] = S\,[L'; t_1, t_2; \alpha] + f(t_1, t_2). \tag{1.42}$$

This may be satisfied by the differential condition:

$$L\,dt = L'\,dt + dW \tag{1.43}$$

where $W = W(\mathbf{x}_1, \dots \mathbf{x}_n; \mathbf{x}'_1, \dots \mathbf{x}'_n; t)$ and dW is the exact differential of W:

$$dW = \frac{\partial W}{\partial t}\,dt + \sum_{jA} \left(\frac{\partial W}{\partial x_{jA}}\,dx_{jA} + \frac{\partial W}{\partial x'_{jA}}\,dx'_{jA} \right).$$

One sees that, in this case:

$$f(t_1, t_2) = W(\mathbf{x}_1(t_2) \dots; t_2) - W(\mathbf{x}_1(t_1), \dots; t_1)$$

and [in view of (1.8a)]: $\delta f = 0$.

From the relations (1.43) and (1.11) it follows that:

$$p_{jA} = \frac{\partial W}{\partial x_{jA}}, \quad p'_{jA} = -\frac{\partial W}{\partial x'_{jA}}, \quad H' = H + \frac{\partial W}{\partial t} \tag{1.44}$$

where $H'(\mathbf{x}'_1, \dots, p'_1, \dots, t)$ is the new Hamiltonian.

These equations determine a canonical transformation. From the first of equations (1.44) there results a functional relationship among the x_{jA}, x'_{jA} and p_{jA}:

$$x'_{jA} = x'_{jA}(x_{11}, p_{11}, \ldots, x_{3n}, p_{3n}; t) \quad j = 1, 2, 3; \quad A = 1, 2, \ldots, n.$$

The latter equations together with the second (1.44) give rise to the following ones:

$$p'_{jA} = p'_{jA}(x_{11}, p_{11}, \ldots, x_{3n}, p_{3n}; t).$$

The *Hamilton–Jacobi equation* allows the determination of the function W—the *generating function* of the canonical transformation in question. It is obtained by the requirement that $H' = 0$:

$$H\left(x_{11}, \ldots, x_{3n}, \frac{\partial W}{\partial x_{11}}, \ldots, \frac{\partial W}{\partial x_{3n}}; t\right) + \frac{\partial W}{\partial t} = 0 \tag{1.45}$$

so that the new coordinates and momenta are constants of motion:

$$\dot{x}'_{jA} = 0, \qquad \dot{p}'_{jA} = 0$$

The integral $W(\mathbf{x}_1, \ldots, \mathbf{x}_n; \mathbf{x}'_1, \ldots, \mathbf{x}'_n; t)$ of the equation (1.45) will contain $3n$ constants x'_{jA} and another set of $3n$ constants given by the second equations (1.44).

1.7 INFINITESIMAL CANONICAL TRANSFORMATIONS

In general, a mapping of a space Σ into another, Σ', is continuous at the point $x_0 \in \Sigma$ if to an arbitrary neighborhood $N(f(x_0), \varepsilon)$, of radius ε, of the point $f(x_0)$ there corresponds a neighborhood $N(x_0, \delta)$ of the point x_0, the transformed (image) of which is contained in $N(f(x_0), \varepsilon)$. In other words, if $f(x) \to f(x_0)$ when $x \to x_0$.[(3)] A continuous transformation is a continuous function of its parameters. Thus, a rotation in 3-dimensional real space is a continuous function of three independent parameters a_{jk} [see (1.27), (1.28)], a Galilei transformation is a continuous function of the three parameters v_j (1.34a).

Clearly an infinitesimal transformation maps every point x_0 of the set in which it is defined into another one arbitrarily near x_0.

Let $\varepsilon_{(k)}$ be the set of (infinitesimal) parameters of an infinitesimal canonical transformation. This means that one restricts oneself to those mappings (1.36) which can be put in the form:

$$\begin{aligned} x'_{jA} &= x_{jA} + \delta x_{jA} \\ p'_{jA} &= p_{jA} + \delta p_{jA} \end{aligned} \tag{1.46}$$

where

$$\delta x_{jA} = \sum_k \varepsilon_{(k)} \left(\frac{\partial x'_{jA}}{\partial \varepsilon_{(k)}} \right)_0$$

$$\delta p_{jA} = \sum_k \varepsilon_{(k)} \left(\frac{\partial p'_{jA}}{\partial \varepsilon_{(k)}} \right)_0, \quad j = 1, 2, 3; \quad A = 1, \ldots, n.$$

The index 0 stands for all $\varepsilon_{(k)} = 0$ in the derivatives. Thus, for a dynamical variable F, δF is proportional to $\varepsilon_{(k)}$ whereas dF is proportional to dt.

Let δW be the Hamilton–Jacobi function for an infinitesimal transformation; one has in view of equations (1.11), (1.43), (1.46):

$$d(\delta W) = -\sum_{jA} [p_{jA} d(\delta x_{jA}) + \delta p_{jA}\, dx_{jA}] + \delta H\, dt \tag{1.47}$$

where $\delta H = H' - H$.

The definition of functions $U_{(k)}(x_{11}, \ldots; p_{11}, \ldots; t)$ by the relationship:

$$\delta W = -\sum_{jA} p_{jA}\, \delta x_{jA} + \sum_k \varepsilon_{(k)} U_{(k)} \tag{1.48}$$

gives rise, in view of (1.47) and (1.46) to the equation:

$$\sum_{jA} \left[\frac{\partial U_{(k)}}{\partial x_{jA}} \dot{x}_{jA} + \frac{\partial U_{(k)}}{\partial p_{jA}} \dot{p}_{jA} \right] + \frac{\partial U_{(k)}}{\partial t}$$

$$= \sum_{jA} \left[-\left(\frac{\partial p'_{jA}}{\partial \varepsilon_{(k)}} \right)_0 \dot{x}_{jA} + \left(\frac{\partial x'_{jA}}{\partial \varepsilon_{(k)}} \right)_0 \dot{p}_{jA} \right] + \left(\frac{\partial H}{\partial \varepsilon_{(k)}} \right)_0 .$$

The following are, therefore, the equations which the functions $U_{(k)}$ satisfy and define an infinitesimal canonical transformation:

$$\left.\begin{aligned} \left(\frac{\partial x'_{jA}}{\partial \varepsilon_{(k)}} \right)_0 &= \frac{\partial U_{(k)}}{\partial p_{jA}} \\ \left(\frac{\partial p'_{jA}}{\partial \varepsilon_{(k)}} \right)_0 &= -\frac{\partial U_{(k)}}{\partial x_{jA}} \\ \left(\frac{\partial H'}{\partial \varepsilon_{(k)}} \right)_0 &= \frac{\partial U_{(k)}}{\partial t}. \end{aligned}\right\} \tag{1.49}$$

It was, in fact, to get equations (1.49), similar to canonical equations (1.12), that the functions $U_{(k)}$—the *generators* of the canonical transformation—were introduced by means of the relationship (1.48).

1.8 TRANSFORMATION OF DYNAMICAL VARIABLES UNDER THE GROUP OF CANONICAL TRANSFORMATIONS; GENERATORS OF TIME AND SPACE TRANSLATIONS AND OF ROTATIONS

Let $F(x, p; t)$ be a dynamical variable [where $x = (x_{11}, \ldots, x_{3n})$, $p = (p_{11}, \ldots, p_{3n})$] such that, for a canonical transformation (1.36) one has, according to (1.39):

$$F'(x', p'; t) = F(x(x', p'), p(x', p'); t).$$

In the case of an infinitesimal transformation (1.46), one can write:

$$F'(x', p'; t) \equiv F'(x + \delta x, p + \delta p; t)$$

or

$$F'(x', p'; t) = F'(x, p; t) + \sum_{kjA} \varepsilon_{(k)} \left[\frac{\partial F'}{\partial x'_{jA}} \frac{\partial x'_{jA}}{\partial \varepsilon_{(k)}} + \frac{\partial F'}{\partial p'_{jA}} \frac{\partial p'_{jA}}{\partial \varepsilon_{(k)}} \right]_0$$

up to terms in the first power of the ε's. We shall then have, in view of the equations (1.49):

$$\delta F = \sum \varepsilon_{(k)} \{F, U_{(k)}\} \tag{1.50}$$

where

$$\delta F = F'(x', p'; t) - F'(x, p; t) = F(x(x', p'), p(x', p'); t) - F'(x, p; t) \tag{1.50a}$$

$$\lim_{\varepsilon \to 0} \frac{\partial F'}{\partial x'_{jA}} = \frac{\partial F}{\partial x_{jA}}, \quad \lim_{\varepsilon \to 0} \frac{\partial F'}{\partial p'_{jA}} = \frac{\partial F}{\partial p_{jA}}.$$

The equation (1.50) states that the *change in form of the dynamical variables F* corresponding to an infinitesimal canonical mapping of the coordinates and momenta, at a given time, *is determined by the Poisson bracket of F with the generators of this mapping.*

We shall now proceed to identify the generating functions of the simplest canonical transformations.

1.8.1 *The Hamiltonian is the generator of an infinitesimal time displacement* (and a movement is the successive composition of such infinitesimal transformations).

In fact, the identification of the parameter ε with dt gives:

$$\delta x_{jA} = \left(\frac{\partial x'_{jA}}{\partial t}\right) dt \Big]_{t=0}$$

$$\delta p_{jA} = \left(\frac{\partial p'_{jA}}{\partial t}\right) dt \Big]_{t=0}$$

or

$$x'_{jA}(t, \varepsilon) \equiv x_{jA}(t + dt)$$

$$p'_{jA}(t, \varepsilon) = p_{jA}(t + dt)\,.$$

The equations (1.49) show that we can, in fact, identify the generator U with the Hamiltonian:

$$U = H \quad \text{for} \quad \varepsilon = dt\,. \tag{1.51}$$

In this case the reader will show the validity of the equation:

$$\frac{dF}{dt} = \frac{\partial F}{\partial t} + \{F, H\} \tag{1.51a}$$

[by considering $F'(x + dx, p + dp; t + dt)$].

1.8.2 *The total momentum of a system of point-particles is the generator of an infinitesimal space translation.*

Here the parameters $\varepsilon_{(k)}$ are the three infinitesimal components of an ordinary vector:

$$x'_{jA} = x_{jA} + \varepsilon_j, \quad j = 1, 2, 3; \quad A = 1, \ldots, n$$

Therefore

$$\frac{\partial x'_{jA}}{\partial \varepsilon_k} = \delta_{jk}$$

for all particles A, whence, according to (1.49):

$$\frac{\partial U_k}{\partial p_{jA}} = \delta_{jk}$$

$$\frac{\partial U_k}{\partial x_{jA}} = 0$$

that is to say

$$U_k \equiv P_k = \sum_{A=1}^{n} p_{kA}, \quad k = 1, 2, 3\,. \tag{1.52}$$

1.8.3 *The generator of an infinitesimal rotation of the coordinate system around the origin is the angular momentum of our system of point-particles.*

For such a rotation the parameters a_{jk} in (1.25) will differ from δ_{jk} by very little:

$$a_{jk} = \delta_{jk} + \varepsilon_{jk}.$$

The orthogonality condition (1.27) requires that the parameters ε_{jk} be anti-symmetric:

$$\varepsilon_{jk} = -\varepsilon_{kj}, \quad k, j = i, 2, 3.$$

The three independent values of this tensor are the parameters of the group. In association with these are the generators U_{jk}, defined by a trivial extension of the equation (1.48):

$$\delta W = -\sum_{jA} p_{jA}\, \delta x_{jA} + \tfrac{1}{2} \sum_{kl} \varepsilon_{kl} U_{kl}$$

$$U_{kl} = -U_{lk}.$$

Then the equations which define these mappings, corresponding to (1.49) are now:

$$\left(\frac{\partial x'_{jA}}{\partial \varepsilon_{kl}}\right)_0 = \frac{\partial U_{kl}}{\partial p_{jA}}$$

$$\left(\frac{\partial p'_{jA}}{\partial \varepsilon_{kl}}\right)_0 = \frac{\partial U_{kl}}{\partial x_{jA}}$$

which, in view of the equations:

$$x'_{jA} = x_{jA} + \varepsilon_{jk} x_{kA}$$

are satisfied by the generator:

$$U_{lk} \equiv L_{kl} = \sum_{A=1}^{n} (x_{kA} p_{lA} - x_{lA} p_{kA}) \tag{1.53}$$

where L_{kl} are the components of the orbital angular momentum of the system of point-particles.

The reader will be able to verify, in the simple example where the dynamical variable is a position coordinate:

$$F_j(x, p) = x_j$$

that

$$F'_j(x', p') = F_j(x(x', p'), p(x', p')) = x'_j - \varepsilon_{jk} x'_k$$

and hence

$$F'_j(x, p) = x_j - \varepsilon_{jk} x_k$$

$$\delta F_j = F_j(x, p) - F'_j(x, p) = \varepsilon_{jk} x_k$$

which coincides with $\frac{1}{2}\varepsilon_{kl} \{F_j, U_{kl}\}$ and (1.53).

1.9 FUNDAMENTAL THEOREM ON SYMMETRIES AND CONSTANTS OF MOTION

If the Hamiltonian of a mechanical system is invariant under all transformations of a canonical group G, the generators of this group are constants of motion.

Let us, in fact, consider equation (1.50) and set

$$F = H$$

under the assumption that:

$$\delta H = 0 \tag{1.54}$$

or [see (1.47)]

$$H' = H.$$

It follows from equation (1.50) that, for arbitrary values of the parameters $\varepsilon_{(k)}$:

$$\{H, U_{(k)}\} = 0. \tag{1.54a}$$

On the other hand, the last of the equations (1.49) and the requirement (1.54) imply that the generators $U_{(k)}$ do not depend explicitly on time:

$$\frac{\partial U_{(k)}}{\partial t} = 0.$$

Therefore, from the relation (1.51a):

$$\frac{dU_{(k)}}{dt} = \frac{\partial U_{(k)}}{\partial t} + \{U_{(k)}, H\}$$

one concludes that the $U_{(k)}$'s are constants of motion:

$$\frac{dU_{(k)}}{dt} = 0.$$

The following two well-known results are, thus, corollaries of this theorem:

Any mechanical system of point-particles the Hamiltonian of which is invariant with respect to the group of translations, admits of its total momentum (1.52) as constant of motion.

If the invariance of the Hamiltonian is under the group of rotations, the constants of motion will be the components of the angular momentum of the system (1.53).

A group is said to be a *symmetry group of the (Hamiltonian of the) system if its generators satisfy the equation* (1.54a).

The group of inhomogeneous orthogonal transformations (translations plus rotations) as a symmetry group determines, therefore, the linear and angular momenta of the system as constants of motion.

Finally, let us note the following Poisson brackets between the generators of space translations and rotations, (1.52) and (1.53):

$$\{P_j, P_k\} = 0$$

$$\{P_j, L_{kl}\} = \delta_{jl}P_k - \delta_{jk}P_l$$

$$\{L_{ij}, L_{kl}\} = \delta_{ik}L_{jl} + \delta_{jl}L_{ik} - \delta_{il}L_{jk} - \delta_{jk}L_{il}\,.$$

If one identifies the three components of the total orbital angular momentum of a system of point-particles, L_x, L_y, L_z, with:

$$L_x = L_{23}, \quad L_y = L_{31}, \quad L_z = L_{12}$$

the last relationship leads to

$$\{L_x, L_y\} = L_z$$

$$\{L_z, L_x\} = L_y$$

$$\{L_y, L_z\} = L_x$$

CHAPTER 2

Symmetries in Classical Linear Field Theory

2.1 THE ELECTROMAGNETIC LAWS AND THE GALILEI RELATIVITY PRINCIPLE

It is well-known that the Galilei relativity principle cannot be extended to the electromagnetic laws. This means that experimental observations do not confirm the transformation laws of the electromagnetic variables corresponding to an assumed invariance of Maxwell's equations under the Galilei group.

These equations have the following form (in the M.K.S. system):

$$\left.\begin{aligned} \nabla \cdot \mathbf{D} &= \varrho \\ \nabla \cdot \mathbf{B} &= 0 \\ \nabla \times \mathbf{E} + \frac{\partial \mathbf{B}}{\partial t} &= 0 \\ \nabla \times \mathbf{H} - \frac{\partial \mathbf{D}}{\partial t} &= \mathbf{j} \end{aligned}\right\} \tag{2.1}$$

where ϱ and j are the charge and current densities, and **E**, **D** and **H**, **B** are the electric and magnetic pairs of field and induction, respectively. The dot indicates as usual the scalar product and the sign $\times$, the vector product.

A transformation from a reference frame S to a Galilei-transformed frame S':

$$\mathbf{x}' = \mathbf{x} - \mathbf{v}t \qquad t' = t \tag{2.2}$$

gives the following relationship between differential operators:

$$\begin{aligned} \nabla &= \nabla' \\ \frac{\partial}{\partial t} &= \frac{\partial}{\partial t'} - \mathbf{v} \cdot \nabla' \end{aligned} \tag{2.2a}$$

The application of (2.2a) into (2.1) and a comparison with Maxwell's equations, assumed valid in the frame S', lead to the transformation equations:

$$\left.\begin{aligned} \varrho' &= \varrho \\ \mathbf{j}' &= \mathbf{j} - \varrho\mathbf{v} \\ \mathbf{D}' &= \mathbf{D} \\ \mathbf{E}' &= \mathbf{E} + \mathbf{v}\times\mathbf{B} \\ \mathbf{B}' &= \mathbf{B} \\ \mathbf{H}' &= \mathbf{H} - \mathbf{v}\times\mathbf{D} \end{aligned}\right\} \tag{2.3}$$

For the potentials ϕ, $\mathbf{A}$, given by:

$$\mathbf{E} = -\nabla\phi - \frac{\partial \mathbf{A}}{\partial t}$$

$$\mathbf{B} = \nabla\times\mathbf{A}$$

one obtains

$$\mathbf{A}' = \mathbf{A}, \qquad \phi' = \phi - \mathbf{v}\cdot\mathbf{A} \tag{2.4}$$

On the other hand, as is well known,[4] the invariance of the phase of a radiation plane wave:

$$\mathbf{A} = \mathbf{A}_0 \cos(\mathbf{k}\cdot\mathbf{x} - \omega t) \tag{2.5}$$

with angular frequency ω, wave factor $\mathbf{k}$ and velocity c in the frame S, gives rise, under the Galilei transformations (2.2), to the following relationship between ω and ω':

$$\omega' = \omega\left(1 - \frac{\mathbf{v}\cdot\mathbf{k}}{ck}\right) \tag{2.6}$$

and between c and c':

$$c' = c\left(1 - \frac{\mathbf{v}\cdot\mathbf{k}}{ck}\right) \tag{2.6a}$$

All experiments, began with the famous observations by Michelson and Morley, as is well known, deny the validity of relations such as (2.3), (2.4), (2.6), (2.6a), based on an assumed invariance of electromagnetic laws under the Galilei group.

2.2 EINSTEIN'S RELATIVITY PRINCIPLE AND THE LORENTZ AND POINCARÉ GROUPS

Lorentz and Poincaré discovered the groups of transformations under which the laws of electromagnetism are invariant, in agreement with experiment. And the beautiful work developed by Einstein led to the discovery of the relativity principle valid for all laws of nature: *these laws are the same everywhere and at all times, they do not depend on where nor when they are obtained; they are independent of the directions in space and of the state of motion of the reference frame, as long as this motion is uniform.* As Wigner has said:(2) "Einstein articulated the postulates about the symmetry of space, that is, the equivalence of directions and of different points of space, eloquently".

In elementary textbooks,(5) the special Lorentz transformations which connect a reference frame S to another, S', in uniform translation with respect to S, with a constant velocity v, parallel to axis Ox (which coincides with $O'x'$) are established. These formulae read:

$$\left.\begin{aligned} x' &= \gamma\,(x - vt) \\ y' &= y \\ z' &= z \\ t' &= \gamma\left(t - \frac{v}{c^2}\,x\right) \\ \gamma &= (1 - \beta^2)^{-1/2}, \quad \beta = \frac{v}{c} \end{aligned}\right\} \qquad (2.7)$$

where c is the velocity of light in vacuum. If β^2 is negligible as compared to the unity, these formulae go over into those of Galilei. And it is now a simple exercise, by the use of the method pointed out in the preceding paragraph, to deduce the (experimentally verified) transformation laws of the electromagnetic field and of the frequency of a plane wave corresponding to the relations (2.7).

It follows from (2.7) that a length and a time interval between two events are not invariant quantities. The fact that a space distance between two simultaneous events for an observer S generates a time distance between the same events for another S', leads one to accept, as a natural generalisation, the fusion of ordinary space and time into a four-dimensional "space–time" linear vector space. Let us call $x^0 = ct$, $x^1 = x$, $x^2 = y$, $x^3 = z$, the coordinates of a point of this space, referred to a given frame.

In general, the Lorentz group is the set of linear, homogeneous transformations which map space–time on to space–time:

$$x'^{\alpha} = l^{\alpha}_{\beta} x^{\beta} \tag{2.8}$$

and which preserves the scalar product of two four-vectors, as defined, the latter, by the bilinear form:

$$(x|y) = x^{\mu} y^{\nu} g_{\mu\nu} \tag{2.9}$$

where we are having in mind a summation over repeated indices from 0 to 3; and:

$$g_{00} = -g_{11} = -g_{22} = -g_{33} = 1; \quad g_{\alpha\beta} = 0 \quad \text{for} \quad \alpha \neq \beta \tag{2.10}$$

The condition:

$$(x'|y') = (x|y) \tag{2.11}$$

imposes the following restrictions on the Lorentz coefficients l^{α}_{β}:

$$l^{\alpha}_{\mu} g_{\alpha\beta} l^{\beta}_{\nu} = g_{\mu\nu}. \tag{2.12}$$

It is seen that the square of the norm of a vector:

$$(x|x) = (x^0)^2 - (\mathbf{x})^2 \tag{2.13}$$

is not positive definite and the condition $(x|x) = 0 \Rightarrow (x) = 0$ is not valid in such a space.

In a notation similar to that introduced in (1.21)–(1.32), we shall express a vector of space–time in terms of a basis $|\lambda_0)$, $|\lambda_1)$, $|\lambda_2)$, $|\lambda_3)$:

$$|x) = x^{\alpha}|\lambda_{\alpha}) \tag{2.14}$$

A Lorentz transformation changes this vector into:

$$|x') = x^{\alpha}|\lambda'_{\alpha}) \tag{2.15}$$

where $|\lambda'_{\alpha})$, $\alpha = 0, 1, 2, 3$, are the vectors of the new basis. We have:

$$|x') = x'^{\alpha}|\lambda_{\alpha}). \tag{2.15a}$$

Call $(y|$ a vector of the dual space

$$(y| = y^{\alpha}(\lambda_{\alpha}| \tag{2.16}$$

and denote by $g_{\mu\nu}$ the scalar product $(\lambda_{\mu}|\lambda_{\nu})$:

$$(\lambda_{\mu}|\lambda_{\nu}) = g_{\mu\nu} = g_{\mu\nu}. \tag{2.17}$$

It follows from (2.15) and (2.15a) that:

$$x'^{\alpha} g_{\alpha\beta} = x^{\nu} (\lambda_{\beta}|\lambda'_{\nu}) \tag{2.18}$$

If a new (contravariant) tensor $g^{\alpha\beta}$ is introduced by the equations:

$$g_{\alpha\eta} g^{\eta\beta} = \delta^{\beta}_{\alpha} = \delta^{\beta}_{\alpha} \tag{2.19}$$

where δ^{α}_{β} is the unit matrix:

$$\delta^{\beta}_{\alpha} = \begin{cases} 1 & \text{for} \quad \alpha = \beta \\ 0 & \text{for} \quad \alpha \neq \beta \end{cases}$$

one obtains from (2.18) and (2.19):

$$x'^{\mu} = x^{\alpha} (\lambda_{\beta}|\lambda'_{\alpha}) \, g^{\beta\mu} . \tag{2.20}$$

Let us call:

$$(\lambda^{\mu}| = (\lambda_{\nu}| g^{\nu\mu}$$

and

$$l^{\mu}_{\alpha} = (\lambda^{\mu}|\lambda'_{\alpha}) .$$

Formula (2.20) reduces to (2.8).

Usually one postulates the Lorentz metric tensor (2.17), (2.10), the scalar product (2.9) and the contravariant tensor $g^{\alpha\beta}$ (2.19). Clearly, one can also write (2.9) under the form:

$$(x|y) = x^{\alpha} y_{\alpha}$$

where

$$y_{\alpha} = g_{\alpha\beta} y^{\beta}$$

and the vector (2.14) can also be written:

$$|x) = x_{\alpha} |\lambda^{\alpha}) .$$

In view of the identification of the numbers x^{μ} with real coordinates ($x^0 = ct$, $x^1 = x$, $x^2 = y$, $x^3 = z$), the Lorentz group matrix $l = \{l^{\mu}_{\nu}\}$ is formed of real numbers. It is well known that an alternative way to represent the Lorentz transformations is obtained by replacing the $g_{\mu\nu}$ elements in (2.17) by the unit matrix elements $\delta_{\mu\nu}$ and at the same time identifying the coordinates x^{μ} with $x^4 = x_4 = ict$, $x^1 = x_1 = x$, $x^2 = x_2 = y$, $x^3 = x_3 = z$, the scalar product of two such vectors being defined as:

$$(x, y) = -(x|y) = x_1 y_1 + x_2 y_2 + x_3 y_3 + x_4 y_4 = \mathbf{x} \cdot \mathbf{y} - x_0 y_0$$

In this case the transformation parameters, represented by $a_{\mu\nu}$:

$$x'_\mu = a_{\mu\nu} x_\nu$$

are not real numbers (a_{jk} and a_{44} are real numbers, a_{4j} and a_{j4} are pure imaginary numbers, where $j, k = 1, 2, 3$).

A consequence of the equations (2.12) is that the determinant of the matrix $\{l^\mu_\nu\}$ is ± 1 since

$$[\det \{l^\mu_\nu\}]^2 = 1\,.$$

The equations (2.12) give, for $\mu = \nu = 0$:

$$l^\alpha_0 g_{\alpha\beta} l^\beta_0 = 1$$

whence:

$$(l^0_0)^2 = 1 + \sum_{\alpha=0}^{3} (l^\alpha_0)^2 \geqq 1$$

that is to say:

$$l^0_0 \geqq 1 \quad \text{or} \quad l^0_0 \leqq -1\,.$$

One is thus led to distinguish four components of the Lorentz group L (the lower sign is that of the determinant, the upper sign indicates the direction of time flow):

(1) the proper orthochronous component L^+_+ the elements of which, $l = \{l^\mu_\nu\}$ are such that:

$$\det l = +1, \qquad l^0_0 \geqq 1$$

(2) the proper non-orthochronous component L^-_+ for which

$$\det l = +1, \qquad l^0_0 \leqq -1$$

(3) the improper orthochronous component L^+_-:

$$\det l = -1, \qquad l^0_0 \geqq 1$$

(4) the improper non-orthochronous component L^-_-:

$$\det l = -1, \qquad l^0_0 \leqq -1\,.$$

It is clear that the first component, L^+_+, is a subgroup of L, the *proper orthochronous group* L^+_+; it contains the identity ($l^\mu_\nu = \delta^\mu_\nu$) and an element of this group can be obtained from any other element of L^+_+ by a continuous variation of the six parameters. The sets L^-_+, L^+_-, L^-_-, above are obviously not groups since they do not contain the identity. The sum or union of these sets with $L_+^\uparrow$ are groups:

$$\left.\begin{aligned} &(a)\ L_+ = L_+^\uparrow \cup L_+^\downarrow \quad \text{(proper Lorentz group)} \\ &(b)\ L^\uparrow = L_+^\uparrow \cup L_-^\uparrow \quad \text{(orthochronous group)} \\ &(c)\ L_0 = L_+^\uparrow \cup L_-^\downarrow \quad \text{(orthochorous group)} \end{aligned}\right\} \tag{2.21}$$

The orthochronous proper Lorentz group $L_+^\uparrow$ is formed of elements which transform a positive time-like vector x:

$$(x|x) = (x^0)^2 - (\mathbf{x})^2 > 0, \qquad x^0 > 0$$

into another positive time-like vector:

$$x'^\mu = l^\mu_\nu x^\nu$$

$$(x'|x') > 0, \qquad x'^0 > 0$$

A space-like surface σ is formed of points such that the distance between any two of them, x and y, in space-time is negative:

$$(x - y|x - y) = (x^0 - y^0)^2 - (\mathbf{x} - \mathbf{y})^2 < 0.$$

A particular space-like surface is a plane perpendicular to the time-axis. For any two points of σ, one is always outside of the light-cone of the other, the light-cone at the origin being the set of points x such that:

$$(x|x) = 0.$$

Given the fact that the four-dimensional volume d^4x is invariant, since:

$$d^4x' = \left|\frac{\partial x'}{\partial x}\right| d^4x \tag{2.22}$$

and

$$\left|\frac{\partial x'}{\partial x}\right| = \det\{l^\mu_\nu\} = 1$$

an integral of the form $\int F(x)\, d^4x$ has the transformation properties of $F(x)$. The integral which generalises a three-dimensional sum is:

$$\int_\sigma f_\lambda(x)\, d\sigma^\lambda$$

where

$$d\sigma^\lambda = (dx^1\, dx^2\, dx^3,\ dx^2\, dx^3\, dx^0,\ dx^3\, dx^1\, dx^0,\ dx^1\, dx^2\, dx^0)$$

is a vector normal in each point of σ. The surface being space-like, $d\sigma^\lambda$ is a time-like vector.

In the special case when σ is a plane perpendicular to the time-axis one has:

$$\int_\sigma f_\lambda \, d\sigma^\lambda \to \int_V f_0 \, d^3x \, .$$

The generalisation of the Gauss theorem to space–time is:

$$\int_W \frac{\partial f^\lambda}{\partial x^\lambda} \, d^4x = \int_{\sigma_2} f^\lambda \, d\sigma_\lambda - \int_{\sigma_1} f^\lambda \, d\sigma_\lambda \qquad (2.23)$$

where W is a four-dimensional region bounded by the space-like surfaces σ_2 and σ_1.

To each of the Lorentz groups (2.21) is associated a *Poincaré group*, the corresponding inhomogeneous Lorentz group. Thus the proper orthochronous Poincaré group P_+ is composed of the elements $\{a, l\}$ such that:

$$x'^\mu = a^\mu + l^\mu_\nu x^\nu$$

where

$$\det l = +1 \qquad l^0_0 > 1 \, .$$

If a Lorentz transformation is defined by six independent parameters l^μ_ν, the corresponding Poincaré transformation is determined by ten parameters a^μ, l^μ_ν.

Clearly, if:

$$x''^\mu = a^\mu_1 + l^\mu_{1\nu} x'^\nu$$

$$x'^\nu = a^\nu_2 + l^\nu_{2\lambda} x^\lambda$$

one gets:

$$x''^\mu = a^\mu_1 + l^\mu_{1\nu} a^\nu_2 + l^\mu_{1\nu} l^\nu_{2\lambda} x^\lambda \, .$$

It is, thus, seen that the multiplication law for the Poincaré group is:

$$\{a_1, l_1\} \, \{a_2, l_2\} = \{a_1 + l_1 a_2, l_1 l_2\} \, .$$

2.3 LORENTZ-COVARIANT FORM OF MAXWELL'S EQUATIONS

The physical basis of the covariant form of Maxwell's equations is the fact that the electric charge of a physical system is Lorentz-invariant. If $\varrho(x)$ is the density of a charge distribution in a frame S we must have:

$$\varrho(x) \, d^3x = \varrho'(x') \, d^3x'$$

where the dash indicates the values measured by an observer of a frame S'. A comparison with the equation (2.22) shows that ϱ transforms like a time coordinate. Thus

$$\mathbf{j} = \varrho\mathbf{v} = \varrho c \frac{d\mathbf{x}}{dx^0}$$

transforms like $d\mathbf{x}$. Therefore the four quantities:

$$j^\mu = (\mu_0 c\varrho, \mu_0\mathbf{j})$$

where

$$c^2 = \frac{1}{\varepsilon_0\mu_0}$$

are the components of a four-vector:

$$j'^\mu(x') = l^\mu_\nu j^\nu(x)\,.$$

The continuity equation:

$$\frac{\partial\varrho}{\partial t} + \nabla\cdot\mathbf{j} = 0$$

is written

$$\frac{\partial j^\lambda}{\partial x^\lambda} = 0$$

where the sum over a repeated index is understood.

Define a quantity $H^{\mu\nu}$ in the following way:

$$H^{0k} = -H^{k0} = \mu_0 c D^k$$

$$H^{23} = -H^{32} = \mu_0 H_x, \quad H^{31} = -H^{13} = \mu_0 H_y, \quad H^{12} = -H^{21} = \mu_0 H_z$$

where D^k, $k = 1, 2, 3$ are the components of the electric displacement vector and H_x, H_y, H_z those of the magnetic field. The equations:

$$\nabla\cdot\mathbf{D} = \varrho, \quad \nabla\times\mathbf{H} - \frac{\partial\mathbf{D}}{\partial t} = \mathbf{j}$$

can be synthetized into

$$\frac{\partial H^{\mu\nu}}{\partial x^\nu} = j^\mu\,.$$

The vector character of j^μ leads to $H^{\mu\nu}$ being the components of a tensor:

$$H'^{\mu\nu}(x') = l^\mu_\alpha l^\nu_\beta H^{\alpha\beta}(x)$$

In the same way, the equations:

$$\nabla \cdot \mathbf{B} = 0, \quad \nabla \times \mathbf{E} + \frac{\partial \mathbf{B}}{\partial t} = 0$$

result from the equations:

$$\frac{\partial F^{\mu\nu}}{\partial x^\lambda} + \frac{\partial F^{\lambda\mu}}{\partial x^\nu} + \frac{\partial F^{\nu\lambda}}{\partial x^\mu} = 0$$

where $F^{\mu\nu}$ is a tensor defined by:

$$F^{k0} = -F^{0k} = -c\varepsilon_0\mu_0 E^k$$

$$F^{23} = -F^{32} = B_x, \quad F^{31} = -F^{13} = B_y, \quad F^{12} = -F^{21} = B_z.$$

Finally, if one sets:

$$a_k = A_k, \qquad a_0 = c\varepsilon_0\mu_0\phi$$

where ϕ is the so-called scalar potential, A_k the vector-potential, the equations which define these:

$$\mathbf{B} = \nabla \times \mathbf{A} \qquad \mathbf{E} = -\nabla\phi - \frac{\partial \mathbf{A}}{\partial t}.$$

can be written:

$$F^{\mu\nu} = \frac{\partial a^\nu}{\partial x_\mu} - \frac{\partial a^\mu}{\partial x^\nu}$$

The equations for the four-vector a^μ, are, when $\varepsilon = \mu = 1$:

$$\Box\, a^\mu = j^\mu, \qquad \frac{\partial a^\mu}{\partial x^\mu} = 0 \tag{2.24}$$

where

$$\Box = g^{\mu\nu} \frac{\partial}{\partial x^\mu} \frac{\partial}{\partial x^\nu} = \frac{1}{c^2} \frac{\partial^2}{\partial t^2} - \nabla^2 \tag{2.24a}$$

is the scalar D'Alembertian operator:

$$\Box' = \Box$$

2.4 THE LAGRANGIAN FORMALISM FOR THE ELECTROMAGNETIC FIELD

The equations of a free particle are:

$$\frac{dp^\mu}{ds} = 0$$

where:

$$ds^2 = dz^\mu \, dz_\mu$$

and:

$$p^k = \frac{m_0}{(1-\beta^2)^{1/2}} \frac{dz^k}{dt}, \qquad p^0 = \frac{m_0 c}{(1-\beta^2)^{1/2}}.$$

They are deduced from an action principle:

$$\delta S = 0$$

the action function being:

$$S = \int L \, dt$$

$$L = -m_0 c^2 (1-\beta^2)^{1/2}.$$

How are Lagrange's equations to be related to a field? One searches for a Lagrange function, a scalar constructed with the electromagnetic potential a^μ and its first space–time derivatives:

$$L = L\left(A^\mu(\mathbf{x}, t), \frac{\partial A^\mu}{\partial x^\nu}(\mathbf{x}, t), x\right)$$

If L is assumed to be invariant with respect to the proper orthochronous Poincaré group, it does not depend explicitly on x:

$$L = L(A^\mu(\mathbf{x}, t), A^\mu_{,\nu}) \qquad A^\mu_{,\nu} = \frac{\partial A^\mu}{\partial x^\nu}.$$

By analogy with equation (1.4) one defines the total Lagrangean:

$$\bar{L} = \int L \, d^3x \tag{2.25}$$

and introduces the action function S as:

$$S = \int_{t_1}^{t_2} \bar{L} \, dt = \frac{1}{c} \int_W L \, d^4x.$$

A field distribution A^μ is determined by the solution of the inhomgeneous wave equation (2.24) and appropriate boundary conditions. The action principle states that out of all possible distributions, the physical field is the one which makes S stationary. If, therefore, the set of possible distributions is defined by a parameter α:

$$A^\mu = A^\mu(x; \alpha) \quad \text{where} \quad x = (t, \mathbf{x})$$

and [see (1.6)]:

$$\delta A^\mu = \left(\frac{\partial A^\mu}{\partial \alpha}\right)_0 d\alpha$$

one has

$$\delta S = \frac{1}{c}\int_W \left\{\frac{\partial L}{\partial A^\mu}\,\delta A^\mu + \frac{\partial L}{\partial A^\mu_{,\nu}}\,\delta A^\mu_{,\nu}\right\} d^4x$$

$$= \frac{1}{c}\int_W \left\{\frac{\partial L}{\partial A^\mu}\,\delta A^\mu + \frac{\partial L}{\partial A^\mu_{,\nu}}\,\frac{\partial}{\partial x^\nu}\,\delta A^\mu\right\} d^4x$$

and a partial integration gives:

$$\delta S = \frac{1}{c}\int_\sigma \frac{\partial L}{\partial A^\mu_{,\nu}}\,\delta A^\mu d\sigma^\nu + \frac{1}{c}\int_W \left\{\frac{\partial L}{\partial A^\mu} - \frac{\partial}{\partial x^\nu}\,\frac{\partial L}{\partial A^\mu_{,\nu}}\right\}\delta A^\mu d^4x$$

where σ is the boundary of the four-dimensional region W. The postulate:

$$\delta S = 0$$

under the assumption that $\delta A^\mu = 0$ on σ, gives rise to the field Lagrange's equations:

$$\frac{\partial L}{\partial A^\mu} - \frac{\partial}{\partial x^\nu}\,\frac{\partial L}{\partial A^\mu_{,\nu}} = 0\,. \tag{2.26}$$

In general, the Lagrange function is a sum of three parts: the particles' Lagrangian, the Lagrangian of the free fields and the interaction between fields and particles

$$L = L_{\text{part}} + L_{\text{f}} + L_{\text{int}}\,.$$

The complete action of a point particle in interaction with an electromagnetic field is:

$$S = -m_0 c\int ds + \frac{1}{2}\,\frac{1}{c}\int A^\mu_{,\nu}A_\mu^{;\nu}d^4x - \frac{1}{c}\int j_\mu A^\mu d^4x$$

where

$$j^\mu(x) = ec\int_{-\infty}^{\infty}\frac{dz^\mu}{ds}\,\delta\,(x - z(s))\,ds\,.$$

The interaction term is therefore:

$$S_{\text{int}} = -e\int A^\mu(z)\,\frac{dz_\mu}{ds}\,ds\,.$$

The equations of motion of this system, obtained by variation of the particle's world-line and of the field are, respectively:

$$m_0 c \frac{d}{ds}\left(\frac{dz^\mu}{ds}\right) = eF^{\mu\nu}\frac{dz_\nu}{ds}$$

$$\Box A^\mu = ec\int_{-\infty}^{\infty}\frac{dz^\mu}{ds}\,\delta\,(x - z(s))\,ds.$$

2.5 CANONICAL FORM OF THE FIELD EQUATIONS

The total Lagrangian L (2.25), is a functional of A_μ, $\dot{A}_\mu$:

$$\bar{L} = \int L\,(A^\mu(\mathbf{x}, t), A^\mu_{,\nu}(\mathbf{x}, t))\,d^3x = \bar{L}\,[A_\mu, \dot{A}_\mu]$$

where $\dot{A}^\mu = cA^\mu_{,0}$.

The functional derivative of $\bar{L}$ with respect to A^μ is defined by the following relationship:

$$\frac{\delta\bar{L}}{\delta A^\mu} = \frac{\partial L}{\partial A^\mu} - \frac{\partial}{\partial x^k}\frac{\partial L}{\partial A^\mu_{,k}}$$

with a summation over the index k from 1 to 3. On the other hand, the functional derivative of $\bar{L}$ with respect to $\dot{A}^\mu$ is

$$\frac{\delta\bar{L}}{\delta\dot{A}^\mu} = \frac{\partial L}{\partial_\mu\dot{A}}.$$

These definitions are suggested by a comparison of the variation of $\bar{L}$:

$$\delta\bar{L} = \int\left(\frac{\delta\bar{L}}{\delta A^\mu}\,\delta A^\mu + \frac{\delta\bar{L}}{\delta\dot{A}^\mu}\,\delta\dot{A}^\mu\right)d^3x$$

(which is a generalisation of the differential of a function:

$$d\phi = \sum_k \frac{\partial\phi}{\partial x^k}\,dx^k$$

the three space-coordinates playing the role of continuous indices) with:

$$\delta\bar{L} = \int\delta L\,d^3x = \int\left\{\left(\frac{\partial L}{\partial A^\mu} - \frac{\partial}{\partial x^k}\frac{\partial L}{\partial A^\mu_{,k}}\right)\delta A^\mu + \frac{\partial L}{\partial\dot{A}^\mu}\,\delta\dot{A}^\mu\right\}d^3x$$

up to a term

$$\int \frac{\partial}{\partial x^k}\left(\frac{\partial L}{\partial A^\mu_{,k}}\,\delta A^\mu\right) d^3x$$

which vanishes on the boundary of the integration domain.

The Lagrange's equation (2.26) can be written in the following form:

$$\frac{\delta \bar{L}}{\delta A^\mu(x)} - \frac{\partial}{\partial t}\,\frac{\delta \bar{L}}{\delta \dot{A}^\mu(x)} = 0$$

similar to (1.9).

The canonical conjugate momentum is defined by:

$$\pi_\mu(x) = \frac{\delta \bar{L}}{\delta \dot{A}^\mu(x)}$$

and the Hamiltonian density, by:

$$H = \pi_\mu \dot{A}^\mu - L$$

which is a function of A^μ, $A^\mu_{,k}$, π_μ. The total Hamiltonian is the functional:

$$\bar{H} = \int H\, d^3x = \bar{H}\,[A^\mu, \pi_\mu]\,.$$

It follows from:

$$\delta\bar{H} = \int \left(\frac{\delta \bar{H}}{\delta A^\mu}\,\delta A^\mu + \frac{\delta \bar{H}}{\delta \pi_\mu}\,\delta\pi_\mu\right) d^3x$$

and

$$\delta\bar{H} = \int \left\{\pi_\mu \delta\dot{A}^\mu + \dot{A}^\mu \delta\pi_\mu - \frac{\partial L}{\partial A^\mu}\,\delta A^\mu - \frac{\partial L}{\partial A^\mu_{,k}}\,\delta A^\mu_{,k} - \frac{\partial L}{\delta \dot{A}^\mu}\,\delta \dot{A}_\mu\right\} d^3x$$

$$= \int \{\,\dot{A}^\mu \delta\pi_\mu - \dot{\pi}_\mu \delta A^\mu\}\, d^3x$$

that:

$$\dot{A}^\mu(x) = \frac{\delta\bar{H}}{\delta\pi_\mu(x)}, \qquad \dot{\pi}_\mu(x) = -\frac{\delta\bar{H}}{\delta A^\mu(x)}, \qquad x = (ct, \mathbf{x}) \quad (2.27)$$

which are the field canonical equations.

2.6 THE FIELD'S POISSON BRACKETS. CONSTANTS OF MOTION

Let $F\,[A^\mu, \pi_\mu]$ and $G\,[A^\mu, \pi_\mu]$ be two functionals of $A^\mu(x)$ and $\pi_\mu(x)$. The Poisson bracket, as defined in (1.15), is now extended to this case by the form:

$$\{F, G\} = \int \left(\frac{\delta F}{\delta A^\mu(x)}\,\frac{\delta G}{\delta \pi_\mu(x)} - \frac{\delta F}{\delta \pi_\mu(x)}\,\frac{\delta G}{\delta A^\mu(x)}\right) d^3x\,. \quad (2.28)$$

We can write:

$$A^{\mu}(\mathbf{x}, t) = \int A^{\lambda}(\mathbf{y}, t)\, \delta^{\mu}_{\lambda}\delta(\mathbf{x} - \mathbf{y})\, d^3y$$

whence

$$\frac{\delta A^{\mu}(\mathbf{x}, t)}{\delta A^{\lambda}(\mathbf{y}, t)} = \delta^{\mu}_{\lambda}\delta(\mathbf{x} - \mathbf{y}).$$

By definition, $A_{\mu}(\mathbf{x}, t)$ and $\pi_{\mu}(\mathbf{y}, t)$, at the same instant t, are independent variables:

$$\frac{\delta A^{\mu}(\mathbf{x}, t)}{\delta \pi_{\lambda}(\mathbf{y}, t)} = 0. \tag{2.29}$$

Therefore:

$$\{A^{\mu}(x), \bar{H}\} = \frac{\delta \bar{H}}{\delta \pi_{\mu}(x)}.$$

$$\{\pi_{\mu}(x), \bar{H}\} = -\frac{\delta \bar{H}}{\delta A^{\mu}(x)}$$

These equations and (2.27) lead to the Hamiltonian–Heisenberg classical equations:

$$\dot{A}^{\mu}(x) = \{A^{\mu}(x), \bar{H}\}$$

$$\dot{\pi}^{\mu}(x) = \{\pi^{\mu}(x), \bar{H}\}.$$

The fundamental Poisson brackets of the field variables at the same instant are

$$\left.\begin{aligned} \{A^{\mu}(\mathbf{x}, t), A^{\lambda}(\mathbf{y}, t)\} &= 0 \\ \{\pi_{\mu}(\mathbf{x}, t), \pi_{\lambda}(\mathbf{y}, t)\} &= 0 \\ \{A^{\mu}(\mathbf{x}, t), \pi_{\lambda}(\mathbf{y}, t)\} &= \delta^{\mu}_{\lambda}\delta(\mathbf{x} - \mathbf{y}) \end{aligned}\right\} \tag{2.30}$$

The generator of an infinitesimal canonical transformation, with parameter ε,

$$\left.\begin{aligned} A^{\mu} \to A'^{\mu}(x) &= A^{\mu}(x) + \delta A^{\mu}(x) \\ \pi_{\mu} \to \pi'_{\mu}(x) &= \pi_{\mu}(x) + \delta\pi_{\mu}(x) \\ \delta A^{\mu} &= \varepsilon_{(k)}\left(\frac{\partial A_{\mu}}{\partial \varepsilon_{(k)}}\right)_0 \\ \delta\pi_{\mu} &= \varepsilon_{(k)}\left(\frac{\partial \pi_{\mu}}{\partial \varepsilon_{(k)}}\right)_0 \end{aligned}\right\} \tag{2.31}$$

is a functional $\bar{U}\,[A^\mu, \pi_\mu]$ such that [see (1.49)]:

$$\delta A^\mu = \varepsilon_{(k)} \frac{\delta \bar{U}_{(k)}}{\delta \pi_\mu}, \qquad \delta \pi_\mu = -\varepsilon_{(k)} \frac{\delta \bar{U}_k}{\delta A^\mu}. \tag{2.32}$$

The variation of a quantity $F\,[A^\mu, \pi_\mu]$ which is a functional of the field variables will be given by the equation:

$$\delta F = \int \left(\frac{\delta F}{\delta A^\mu}\, \delta A^\mu + \frac{\delta F}{\delta \pi_\mu}\, \delta \pi_\mu \right) d^3x$$

$$= \varepsilon_{(k)} \int \left(\frac{\delta F}{\delta A^\mu} \frac{\delta \bar{U}_{(k)}}{\delta \pi_\mu} - \frac{\delta F}{\delta \pi_\mu} \frac{\delta \bar{U}_{(k)}}{\delta A^\mu} \right) d^3x$$

hence

$$\delta F = \varepsilon_{(k)} \{F, \bar{U}_{(k)}\}. \tag{2.33}$$

On the other hand, if G is a functional of A^μ and π_μ and a function of t:

$$G = G\,[A^\mu, \pi; t]$$

one has:

$$\frac{dG}{dt} = \frac{\partial G}{\partial t} + \int d^3x \left(\frac{\partial G}{\delta A^\mu}\, \dot{A}^\mu + \frac{\partial G}{\delta \pi_\mu}\, \dot{\pi}_\mu \right)$$

or

$$\frac{dG}{dt} = \frac{\partial G}{\partial t} + \{G, \bar{H}\}. \tag{2.34}$$

It follows from (2.33) and (2.34) that every infinitesimal canonical transformation which leaves the Hamilton an invariant, determines a constant of motion, the generator of the transformation (see equation 1.9).

We shall see later [(2.42), (2.46)] the expression of the generators of translations and rotations, respectively the energy momentum vector and the angular momentum tensor of a field.

2.7 FREE-FIELD POISSON BRACKETS

The Poisson brackets written down in (2.28) refer to field variables taken at the same time, i.e., at different points of a plane perpendicular to the time axis. As such a plane is not an invariant surface, it is of interest to know the Poisson brackets between two fields taken at any two points in space–time. To derive these we need to use the free-field equation.

We have, by definition:

$$\{A^\mu(x), A^\nu(x')\} = \int d^3y \left[\frac{\delta A^\mu(\mathbf{x}, t)\, \delta A^\nu(\mathbf{x}', t')}{\delta A^\lambda(\mathbf{y}, t)\, \delta \pi_\lambda(\mathbf{y}, t\ )} - \frac{\delta A^\mu(\mathbf{x}, t)\, \delta A^\nu(\mathbf{x}', t')}{\delta \pi_\lambda(\mathbf{y}, t)\, \delta A^\lambda(\mathbf{y}, t)}\right]$$

where we have taken the time of the independent variables $A^\lambda(\mathbf{y}, t), \pi_\lambda(\mathbf{y}, t)$ equal to that of $A^\mu(\mathbf{x}, t)$. In virtue of the equation (2.29), this reduces to:

$$\{A^\mu(x), A^\nu(x')\} = \int d^3y\, \frac{\delta A^\mu(\mathbf{x}, t)}{\delta A^\lambda(\mathbf{y}, t)}\, \frac{\delta A^\nu(\mathbf{x}', t')}{\delta \pi_\lambda(\mathbf{y}, t)}.$$

Develop $A^\nu(\mathbf{x}', t')$ in series around t,

$$A^\nu(\mathbf{x}', t') = A^\nu(\mathbf{x}', t) + (t' - t)\left(\frac{\partial A^\nu(\mathbf{x}', t')}{\partial t'}\right)_{t'=t} + \cdots$$

On the other hand, for a free field:

$$L = \tfrac{1}{2} g_{\mu\alpha} g^{\lambda\nu} A^\mu_{,\lambda} A^\alpha_{,\nu}$$

$$\pi_\nu = \frac{1}{c}\, \frac{\partial L}{\partial A^\nu_{,0}} = \frac{1}{c^2}\, g_{\nu\alpha} \dot{A}^\alpha$$

$$g^{\mu\nu}\pi_\nu = \frac{1}{c^2}\, \dot{A}^\mu$$

$$\left(\frac{\partial^2 A^\nu(x', t')}{\partial t'^2}\right)_{t'=t} = c^3 \nabla'^2 A^\nu(\mathbf{x}', t)$$

therefore:

$$\{A^\mu(\mathbf{x}, t), A^\nu(\mathbf{x}', t')\} = \int d^3y\, \delta^\mu_\lambda \delta(\mathbf{x} - \mathbf{y}) \left[\frac{\delta A^\nu(\mathbf{x}', t)}{\delta \pi_\lambda(\mathbf{y}, t)} + (t' - t)\, c^2\, \frac{\delta \pi^\nu(\mathbf{x}', t)}{\delta \pi_\lambda(\mathbf{y}, t)}\right.$$

$$\left. + \frac{1}{2!}\, c^2 (t' - t)^2 \nabla'^2\, \frac{\delta A^\nu(\mathbf{x}', t)}{\delta \pi_\lambda(\mathbf{y}, t)} + \frac{1}{3!}\, c^4 (t' - t)^3 \nabla'^2\, \frac{\delta \pi^\nu(\mathbf{x}', t)}{\delta \pi_\lambda(\mathbf{y}, t)} + \cdots\right]$$

that is

$$\{A^\mu(x), A^\nu(x')\} = c^2 g^{\mu\nu} \sum_{n=0}^{\infty} \frac{1}{(2n+1)!}\, (t' - t)^{2n+1} [c^2 \nabla'^2]^n\, \delta(\mathbf{x}' - \mathbf{x}).$$

The Fourier representation:

$$\delta(\mathbf{x}' - \mathbf{x}) = \frac{1}{(2\pi)^3} \int d^3k \exp[i\mathbf{k} \cdot (\mathbf{x}' - \mathbf{x})]$$

leads to:

$$\{A^\mu(x), A^\nu(x')\} = cg^{\mu\nu} D(x' - x) \tag{2.35}$$

where the Jordan–Pauli function is defined by:

$$D(x - x') = -D(x' - x)$$

$$= \frac{1}{(2\pi)^3} \int d^3k \exp[i\mathbf{k} \cdot (\mathbf{x}' - \mathbf{x})] \frac{1}{k_0} \sin[k_0(x_0' - x_0)].$$

It vanishes if x and x' are on a space-like surface σ and fulfills the conditions:

$$\Box D(x) = 0$$

$$\int_\sigma \frac{\partial D}{\partial x^\mu} d\sigma^\mu = 1$$

$$D(x) = 0 \quad \text{if} \quad (x|x) < 0.$$

If the field $A^\mu(x)$ and its first derivatives $(\partial A^\mu)/(\partial x^\nu)$ are given on a space-like surface, the field will be determined at any point y of space–time by the relation:

$$A^\mu(y) = \int_\sigma \left[D(y - x) \frac{\partial A^\mu(x)}{\partial x^\nu} - A^\mu(x) \frac{\partial}{\partial x^\nu} D(y - x) \right] d\sigma^\nu$$

2.8 NOETHER'S THEOREM

We shall now prove an important theorem due to E.Noether, which allows one to construct the constants of motion associated to the symmetry groups of a field theory. This theorem may be stated as follows:

To every continuous transformation of the (geometrical or dynamical) coordinates of a field, $\psi^{[\alpha]}$, for which the field transformation law is known, a certain combination of $\psi^{[\alpha]}$ and its first derivatives $\psi^{[\alpha]}_{,\lambda}$, is associated which is covariant and conserved in time, if the transformation leaves the action invariant.

Let:

$$x^\mu \to x'^\mu = x^\mu + \delta x^\mu \tag{2.36}$$

be an infinitesimal geometric transformation of the coordinates in space–time defined by a set of parameters $\omega^{[\nu]}$, such that:

$$\delta x^\mu = f^\mu_{[\nu]} \omega^{[\nu]}. \tag{2.37}$$

In the case of a space–time translation, one has:

$$\omega^{[\nu]} = \varepsilon^{\nu} \qquad f^{\mu}_{[\nu]} = \delta^{\mu}_{\nu}. \tag{2.38}$$

For an infinitesimal Lorentz-transformation:

$$\omega^{[\nu]} = \varepsilon^{\nu\lambda} = -\varepsilon^{\lambda\nu}$$

$$f^{\mu}_{[\nu]} \equiv f^{\mu}_{\nu\lambda} = -f^{\mu}_{\lambda\nu} = \tfrac{1}{2}\,(\delta^{\mu}_{\nu} g_{\lambda\alpha} - \delta^{\mu}_{\lambda} g_{\nu\alpha})\, x^{\alpha}.$$

The mappings (2.36) induce a transformation of the field variables:

$$\psi^{[\alpha]}(x) \to \psi'^{[\alpha]}(x') = \psi^{[\alpha]}(x) + \delta\psi^{[\alpha]}(x)$$

The variation $\bar{\delta}\psi^{[\alpha]}(x)$ results from a change in the form of the field function and from a change of x into x'; we shall assume it proportional to the infinitesimal parameters $\omega^{[\beta]}$:

$$\bar{\delta}\psi^{[\alpha]}\,(x) = \mathscr{F}^{[\alpha]}_{[\beta]}(x)\,\omega^{[\beta]}. \tag{2.39}$$

The variations of the fields we considered previously [see (2.31)], are variations in form only:

$$\delta\psi^{[\alpha]}\,(x) = \psi'^{[\alpha]}(x) - \psi^{[\alpha]}(x)$$

i.e., the original and transformed fields are taken at the same point x.

One can express $\delta\psi^{[\alpha]}$ in terms of the parameters $\omega^{[\nu]}$ and of $\mathscr{F}^{[\alpha]}_{[\beta]}(x)\,\omega^{[\beta]}$. Indeed:

$$\begin{aligned}\delta\psi^{[\alpha]}\,(x) &= \psi'^{[\alpha]}(x') - \psi^{[\alpha]}(x) - (\psi'^{[\alpha]}(x') - \psi'^{[\alpha]}(x)) \\ &= [\mathscr{F}^{[\alpha]}_{[\beta]}(x) - \psi^{[\alpha]}_{,\lambda}(x)\, f^{\lambda}_{[\beta]}]\,\omega^{[\beta]}.\end{aligned} \tag{2.40}$$

The action is a functional of the field and of the domain of integration R:

$$S\,[\psi^{[\alpha]}; R] = \int_R L\, d^4x$$

where

$$L = L\,(x; \psi^{[\alpha]}(x), \psi^{[\alpha]}_{,\lambda}(x)).$$

The variation of the action is:

$$\bar{\delta}S = S\,[\psi'^{[\alpha]}; R'] - S\,[\psi^{[\alpha]}; R]$$

and is equal to

$$\bar{\delta}S = S\,[\psi'^{[\alpha]}; R'] - S\,[\psi^{[\alpha]}; R'] + S\,[\psi^{[\alpha]}; R'] - S\,[\psi^{[\alpha]}; R]$$

that is

$$\bar{\delta} S = \int_{R'} L\,(x', \psi'^{[\alpha]}(x'), \psi'^{[\alpha]}_{,\lambda}(x'))\, d^4x' - \int_{R'} L\,(x', \psi^{[\alpha]}(x'), \psi^{[\alpha]}_{,\lambda}(x'))\, d^4x'$$

$$+ \int_{R'} L\,(x', \psi^{[\alpha]}(x'), \psi^{[\alpha]}_{,\lambda}(x'))\, d^4x' - \int_{R} L\,(x, \psi^{[\alpha]}(x), \psi^{[\alpha]}_{,\lambda}(x))\, d^4x$$

where R' is the transformed domain of integration resulting from (2.36).

We thus have:

$$\bar{\delta} S = \int_{R'} \delta L\, d^4x' + \int_{R'} L\,(x', \psi^{[\alpha]}(x'), \psi^{[\alpha]}_{,\lambda}(x'))\, d^4x'$$

$$- \int_{R} L(x, \psi^{[\alpha]}(x), \psi^{[\alpha]}_{,\lambda}(x))\, d^4x$$

hence, if one keeps only terms in first order in the ω's:

$$\bar{\delta} S = \int_{R} d^4x \left(\frac{\partial L}{\partial \psi^{[\alpha]}}\, \delta\psi^{[\alpha]} + \frac{\partial L}{\partial \psi^{[\alpha]}_{,\lambda}}\, \delta\psi^{[\alpha]}_{,\lambda} + \frac{\partial L}{\partial x^\lambda}\, \delta x^\lambda + L\, \frac{\partial}{\partial x^\lambda}\, (\delta x^\lambda) \right).$$

Here we have taken into account that:

$$d^4x' = \left| \frac{\partial x}{\partial x'} \right| d^4x = \left(1 + \frac{\partial}{\partial x^\lambda}\, (\delta x^\lambda) \right) d^4x.$$

Now the field equations:

$$\frac{\partial L}{\partial \psi^{[\alpha]}} - \frac{\partial}{\partial x^\lambda}\, \frac{\partial L}{\partial \psi^{[\alpha]}_{,\lambda}} = 0$$

allows us to write $\bar{\delta} S$ under the following form:

$$\bar{\delta} S = \int \frac{\partial}{\partial x^\lambda} \left[\frac{\partial L}{\partial \psi^{[\alpha]}_{,\lambda}}\, (\mathscr{F}^{[\alpha]}_{[\beta]}(x) - \psi^{[\alpha]}_{,\nu} f^{\nu}_{[\beta]}) + L f^{\lambda}_{[\beta]} \right] \omega^{[\beta]}\, d^4x$$

It is now seen that the postulate of invariance of the action under the transformations in question:

$$\bar{\delta} S = 0$$

for any infinitesimal ω's, leads to the existence of the set of quantities, he Noether tensor $N^{\lambda}_{[\beta]}$:

$$N^{\lambda}_{[\beta]} = \frac{\partial L}{\partial \psi^{[\alpha]}_{,\lambda}}\, (\psi^{[\alpha]}_{,\nu} f^{\nu}_{[\beta]} - \mathscr{F}^{[\alpha]}_{[\beta]}) - L f^{\lambda}_{[\beta]} \tag{2.41}$$

the divergence of which vanishes:

$$\frac{\partial N^{\lambda}_{[\beta]}}{\partial x^{\lambda}} = 0. \tag{2.41a}$$

Therefore, if this equation is integrated over a four-dimensional region between two space-like surfaces σ_1 and σ_2, and if the field quantities which occur in $N^{\lambda}_{[\beta]}$ vanish at infinite space-like distances, we can write, according to Gauss theorem (2.23)

$$\int d^4x \frac{\partial N^{\lambda}_{[\beta]}}{\partial x^{\lambda}} = \int_{\sigma_2} d\sigma_{\lambda} N^{\lambda}_{[\beta]} - \int_{\sigma_1} d\sigma_{\lambda} N^{\lambda}_{[\beta]} = 0.$$

This means that the quantity

$$S_{[\beta]} = \int_{\sigma} d\sigma_{\lambda}\, N^{\lambda}_{[\beta]} \tag{2.41b}$$

does not depend on the space-like surface σ. If this is a plane perpendicular to the time axis, then

$$S_{[\beta]} = \int d^3x\, N^{0}_{[\beta]}$$

does not depend on time, it is a conserved quantity:

$$\frac{dS_{[\beta]}}{dx^0} = 0.$$

Clearly, the Noether tensor $N^{\lambda}_{[\beta]}$ is defined up to a term which contains the divergence of a certain antisymmetric tensor. Indeed, if such a tensor is:

$$t^{\lambda\nu}_{[\beta]}(x) = -t^{\nu\lambda}_{[\beta]}(x)$$

then the two quantities $N^{\lambda}_{[\beta]}$ and $N'^{\lambda}_{[\beta]}$:

$$N'^{\lambda}_{[\beta]} = N^{\lambda}_{[\beta]} + \frac{\partial}{\partial x^{\nu}} t^{\lambda\nu}_{[\beta]}$$

will give rise to the same conserved objects, since:

$$\frac{\partial N'^{\lambda}_{[\beta]}}{\partial x^{\lambda}} = \frac{\partial N^{\lambda}_{[\beta]}}{\partial x^{\lambda}}.$$

2.9 THE FIELD ENERGY–MOMENTUM VECTOR

Suppose now that the transformations (2.36) are translations in space–time by the vector ε^{ν}:

$$\omega^{[\nu]} = \varepsilon^{\nu}, \qquad f^{\mu}_{[\nu]} = \delta^{\mu}_{\nu}.$$

In this case, the field variables are invariant:

$$\psi'^{[\alpha]}(x') = \psi^{[\alpha]}(x)$$

therefore:

$$\mathscr{F}^{[\alpha]}_{[\beta]}(x) \equiv 0.$$

The Noether quantity is the energy–momentum tensor:

$$N^{\alpha}_{[\beta]} \equiv T^{\alpha}_{\beta} = \frac{\partial L}{\partial \psi^{[\nu]}_{,\alpha}} \psi^{[\nu]}_{,\beta} - L\delta^{\alpha}_{\beta}. \tag{2.42}$$

The field energy–momentum four-vector is therefore;

$$P^{\lambda} = g^{\lambda\beta} \int d\sigma_{\alpha} T^{\alpha}_{\beta} = g^{\lambda\beta} \int d^3x T^{0}_{\beta} \tag{2.42a}$$

hence, for the Hamiltonian:

$$\bar{H} = P^0 = \int d^3x \left(\frac{\partial L}{\partial \psi^{[\nu]}_{,0}} \psi^{[\nu]}_{,0} - L \right) = \int d^3x \, (\pi_{[\nu]}\dot{\psi}^{[\nu]} - L) \tag{2.42b}$$

and for the momentum:

$$P^k = g^{kl} \int d^3x T^0_l = c \int d^3x \pi_{[\nu]}\psi^{[\nu],k} = -P_k.$$

If one regards the field equations under the form (2.32), the generators for a space–time translations are $\bar{U}^{\lambda} = -P^{\lambda}$.

2.10 THE FIELD ANGULAR MOMENTUM TENSOR

When the infinitesimal transformations of the coordinates are homogeneous Lorentz transformations:

$$x'^{\alpha} = l^{\alpha}_{\beta} x^{\beta}$$

one has:

$$l^{\alpha}_{\beta} = \delta^{\alpha}_{\beta} + \varepsilon^{\alpha}_{\beta}$$

where the parameters $\varepsilon^{\alpha}_{\beta}$ are to be retained only to first order. We may write:

$$x'^{\alpha} = x^{\alpha} + \varepsilon_{\beta\alpha} x^{\beta}$$

where

$$\varepsilon_{\alpha\beta} = g_{\alpha\lambda}\varepsilon^{\lambda}_{\beta}$$

and, in view of (2.12):

$$\varepsilon_{\alpha\beta} = -\varepsilon_{\beta\alpha}$$

We can still write:

$$\left.\begin{aligned} x'^{\alpha} &= x^{\alpha} + \delta x^{\alpha} \\ \delta x^{\alpha} &= \tfrac{1}{2} f^{\alpha}_{\lambda\nu} \varepsilon^{\lambda\nu} \\ f^{\alpha}_{\lambda\nu} &= -f^{\alpha}_{\nu\lambda} = (\delta^{\alpha}_{\lambda} g_{\nu\eta} - \delta^{\alpha}_{\nu} g_{\lambda\eta})\, x^{\eta} \end{aligned}\right\} \tag{2.43}$$

Now

$$\psi'^{[\alpha]}(x') = \psi^{[\alpha]}(x) + \tfrac{1}{2}\mathscr{F}^{[\alpha]}_{\lambda\nu}(x)\,\varepsilon^{\lambda\nu}$$

and we shall set:

$$\mathscr{F}^{[\alpha]}_{\lambda\nu}(x) = M^{[\alpha]}_{[\beta]\lambda\nu}\psi^{[\beta]}(x) \tag{2.44}$$

where

$$M^{[\alpha]}_{[\beta]\lambda\nu} = -M^{[\alpha]}_{[\beta]\nu\lambda}.$$

The Noether quantity is thus the following:

$$N^{\lambda}_{\mu\nu} = \frac{\partial L}{\partial \psi^{[\alpha]}_{,\lambda}} (\psi^{[\alpha]}_{,\eta} f^{\eta}_{\mu\nu} - \mathscr{F}^{[\alpha]}_{\mu\nu}) - L f^{\lambda}_{\mu\nu}$$

that is, in view of equations (2.41), (2.42) and (2.43):

$$N^{\lambda}_{\mu\nu} = T^{\lambda}_{\mu} x_{\nu} - T^{\lambda}_{\nu} x_{\mu} - \frac{\partial L}{\partial \psi^{[\alpha]}_{,\lambda}} M^{[\alpha]}_{[\beta]\mu\nu}\psi^{[\beta]}.$$

This is the angular momentum tensor density; the first two terms constitute its orbital part, the last term the spin part. The angular momentum tensor is:

$$J_{\mu\nu} = \int d\sigma_{\lambda} N^{\lambda}_{\mu\nu} = \int d^3x\, N^{0}_{\mu\nu} \tag{2.45}$$

The generator of the canonical transformation corresponding to a spatial rotation is:

$$U_{kl} = -J_{kl} \tag{2.46}$$

The reader will verify that the *conservation of the tensor* $N_{\lambda\mu\nu}$ *requires a symmetric energy momentum tensor:* $T_{\mu\nu} = T_{\nu\mu}$.

2.11 THE LORENTZ GEOMETRICAL NATURE OF FIELDS

The study of the representations of the Poincaré group determines the geometrical nature of the wave fields the equations of which are invariant under the proper Poincaré group.(6) The fields must belong to a representation space of this group and they can only be scalars, spinors, vectors and spinors or tensors of higher rank.

Here is a list of the simplest fields (where we take $c = 1$):

2.11.1 Complex scalar field:

$$\phi(x), \phi^*(x) : \phi'(x') = \phi(x)$$

Free field equation:

$$(\Box + K^2)\,\phi(x) = 0 \qquad (\Box + K^2)\,\phi^*(x) = 0$$

Lagrangian:

$$L = -(K^2\phi^*\phi - g^{\mu\nu}\phi^*_{,\mu}\phi_{,\nu})$$

Energy-momentum tensor:

$$\begin{aligned} T^{\mu\nu} &= \frac{\partial L}{\partial \psi^{[\lambda]}_{,\mu}}\,\psi^{[\lambda],\nu} + \frac{\partial L}{\partial \psi^{[\lambda]*}_{,\mu}}\,\psi^{*[\lambda],\nu} - Lg^{\mu\nu} \\ &= g^{\mu\alpha}g^{\nu\beta}\,(\phi^*_{,\alpha}\phi_{,\beta} + \phi^*_{,\beta}\phi_{,\alpha}) - Lg^{\mu\nu} \end{aligned}$$

Hamiltonian and momentum:

$$\pi^* = \frac{\partial L}{\partial \dot{\phi}} = \dot{\phi}^*$$

$$H = \int d^3x\,[\pi^*\pi + (\nabla\phi^* \cdot \nabla\phi) + K^2\phi^*\phi]$$

$$P^k = \int d^3x\,(\pi^*\phi_{,k} + \pi\phi^*_{,k}) = \int d^3x T^{0k}$$

Angular momentum (only orbital since $M^{[\alpha]}_{[\beta]\lambda\nu} = 0$)

$$\begin{aligned} L_{kl} &= \int d^3x\,[\pi^*(\phi_{,k}x_l - \phi_{,l}x_k) + \pi\,(\phi^*_{,k}x_l - \phi^*_{,l}x_k)] \\ &= \int d^3x\,(T_{0k}x_l - T_{0l}x_k). \end{aligned}$$

The two scalars ϕ, ϕ^* are equivalent to the couple of real fields ϕ_1, ϕ_2 such that:

$$\phi = \frac{1}{\sqrt{2}}\,(\phi_1 - i\phi_2)$$

$$\phi^* = \frac{1}{\sqrt{2}}\,(\phi_1 + i\phi_2) \tag{2.47}$$

and one can describe the quantities associated to a single real field by expressing the above ones in terms of ϕ_1, ϕ_2 and dropping the terms in ϕ_2.

2.11.2 Real vector field, $\phi^\mu(x)$:

$$\phi'^\mu(x') = l^\mu_\nu \phi^\nu(x)$$

Free-field equation:

$$(\Box + K^2)\,\phi^\mu(x) = 0 \qquad \phi^\mu_{,\mu} = 0$$

Lagrangian:

$$L = -\tfrac{1}{2} g_{\alpha\beta}\,(K^2 \phi^\alpha \phi^\beta - g^{\mu\lambda} \phi^\alpha_{,\mu} \phi^\beta_{,\lambda}). \tag{2.48}$$

In view of the condition $\phi^\mu_{,\mu} = 0$, one can write (L is defined up to a four-divergence):

$$L = -\tfrac{1}{2} g_{\alpha\beta}\,(K^2 \phi^\alpha \phi^\beta - g^{\mu\lambda} F^\alpha_\mu F^\beta_\lambda)$$

where:

$$F^\alpha_\mu = \frac{\partial \phi_\mu}{\partial x_\alpha} - \frac{\partial \phi^\alpha}{\partial x^\mu}.$$

Energy–momentum tensor:

$$T^\alpha_\beta = g_{\nu\eta} g^{\alpha\lambda} \phi^\eta_{,\lambda} \phi^\nu_{,\beta} - L\delta^\alpha_\beta$$

Hamiltonian and momentum:

$$\pi_\alpha = \frac{\partial L}{\partial \phi^\alpha_{,0}} = g_{\alpha\beta} \phi^\beta_{,0} = \phi_{\alpha,0}$$

$$H = \tfrac{1}{2} \int d^3x\,(\pi_\alpha \pi^\alpha + \phi^\alpha_{,k} + \phi_{\alpha,k} + K^2 \phi_\alpha \phi^\alpha)$$

$$P^k = \int d^3x \pi_\alpha \phi^{\alpha,k} = -P_k$$

Angular momentum:

$$J_{\mu\nu} = \int d^3x N^0_{\mu\nu} = L_{\mu\nu} + S_{\mu\nu}$$

$$L_{\mu\nu} = \int (T^0_\mu x_\nu - T^0_\nu x_\mu)\, d^3x = \int [\pi_\alpha (\phi^\alpha_{,\mu} x_\nu - \phi^\alpha_{,\nu} x_\mu) - L(\delta^0_\mu x_\nu - \delta^0_\nu x_\mu)]\, d^3x$$

$$S_{\mu\nu} = \int (\phi_\mu \pi_\nu - \phi_\nu \pi_\mu)\, d^3x$$

2.11.3 Dirac's spinor field

$$\psi(x) = \begin{pmatrix} \psi_1 \\ \psi_2 \\ \psi_3 \\ \psi_4 \end{pmatrix}$$

We take $\hbar = 1$, $c = 1$.
Free-field equation of motion:

$$\left(i\gamma^\alpha \frac{\partial}{\partial x^\alpha} - K\right)\psi(x) = 0$$

where $\gamma^0, \gamma^1, \gamma^2, \gamma^3$ are four-by-four matrices satisfying

$$\gamma^\mu\gamma^\nu + \gamma^\nu\gamma^\mu = 2g^{\mu\nu}$$

The adjoint field $\overline{\psi}$ is defined by

$$\overline{\psi}(x) = \psi^\dagger(x)\,\gamma^0$$

and $\psi^\dagger$ is the Hermitian conjugate of $\psi : \psi^\dagger = (\psi_1^*, \psi_2^*, \psi_3^*, \psi_4^*)$. Its equation is:

$$i\frac{\partial\overline{\psi}}{\partial x^\mu}\gamma^\mu + K\overline{\psi} = 0 \qquad (\gamma^\mu)^\dagger = \gamma^0\gamma^\mu\gamma^0.$$

The Poincaré transformed of $\psi(x)$ is:

$$\psi'(x') = D(l)\,\psi(x)$$

where

$$l^\mu_\nu D(l)\,\gamma^\nu D^{-1}(l) = \gamma^\mu \tag{2.49}$$

For an infinitesimal transformation one has:

$$l^\mu_\nu = \delta^\mu_\nu + \varepsilon^\mu_\nu$$

$$D_{\alpha\beta}(\varepsilon) = \delta_{\alpha\beta} + \tfrac{1}{2}M^{\lambda\nu}_{\alpha\beta}\varepsilon_{\lambda\nu}. \tag{2.50}$$

It follows from the equations (2.49) and (2.50) that:

$$i\,[M^{\lambda\nu}, \gamma^\eta] = \gamma^\nu g^{\lambda\eta} - \gamma^\lambda g^{\nu\eta}$$

which is satisfied by:

$$M^{\lambda\nu} = \tfrac{1}{4}(\gamma^\lambda\gamma^\nu - \gamma^\nu\gamma^\lambda).$$

The Lagrangian is

$$L = \frac{i}{2}\left(\overline{\psi}\gamma^\mu\frac{\partial\psi}{\partial x^\mu} - \frac{\partial\overline{\psi}}{\partial x^\mu}\gamma^\mu\psi(x)\right) - K\overline{\psi}\psi.$$

The energy–momentum tensor has the form:

$$T^{\lambda\nu} = \frac{i}{2}g^{\alpha\lambda}\left(\overline{\psi}\gamma^\nu\frac{\partial\psi}{\partial x^\alpha} - \frac{\partial\overline{\psi}}{\partial x^\alpha}\gamma^\nu\psi\right)$$

and the spin tensor:

$$S^{\nu;\alpha\beta} = -\frac{\partial L}{\partial \psi_{\lambda,\nu}} M_{\lambda\eta;\alpha\beta}\psi_\eta - \bar{\psi}_\lambda M_{\lambda\eta;\alpha\beta}\frac{\partial L}{\partial \bar{\psi}_{\eta,\nu}} = \frac{1}{4}\bar{\psi}(x)[\gamma^\nu\sigma^{\alpha\beta} + \sigma^{\alpha\beta}\gamma^\nu]\psi(x)$$

where

$$\sigma^{\alpha\beta} = \frac{1}{2i}(\gamma^\alpha\gamma^\beta - \gamma^\beta\gamma^\alpha).$$

2.12 THE CURRENT-VECTOR

When the wave fields are complex functions, the Lagrangian—which must be real (Hermitian in the quantized version of the theory)—must depend only on terms of the form $\psi^{*[\alpha]}\psi_{[\alpha]}$, $g^{\mu\lambda}\psi^{*[\alpha]}_{,\lambda}\psi_{[\alpha],\mu}$. It will therefore be invariant if the field is multiplied by an arbitrary phase factor *(gauge transformations of the first kind):*

$$\psi'^{[\alpha]}(x) = e^{i\eta}\psi^{[\alpha]}(x), \qquad \psi^{*\prime[\alpha]}(x) = e^{-i\eta}\psi^{*[\alpha]}(x)$$

where η is a real number.

This constitutes an example of a non-geometrical group of transformations, the importance of which gives support to the second definition of the invariance principle in paragraph 1.D.

For η infinitesimal we have, up to terms of first order in η:

$$\psi'^{[\alpha]}(x) = (1 + i\eta)\,\psi^{[\alpha]}(x)$$
$$\psi^{*\prime[\alpha]}(x) = (1 - i\eta)\,\psi^{*[\alpha]}(x)$$

As the coordinates x do not change, we have in (2.41):

$$f^{\mu}_{[\nu]} = 0.$$

However (see (2.40)):

$$\mathscr{F}^{[\alpha]}_{[\beta]} \equiv i\psi^{[\alpha]}, \qquad \omega^{[\beta]} = \eta$$

The conserved Noether's quantity is the current-vector:

$$N^\nu \equiv j^\nu = i\left(\frac{\partial L}{\partial \psi^{*[\alpha]}_{,\nu}}\psi^{*[\alpha]} - \frac{\partial L}{\partial \psi^{[\alpha]}_{,\nu}}\psi^{[\alpha]}\right)$$

i.e. such that: $\partial j^\nu/\partial x^\nu = 0$.

The charge of the field is:

$$Q = \int d\sigma_\nu j^\nu = \int d^3x j^0 .$$

Thus the current-vector of a complex scalar field is:

$$j^\nu = ig^{\nu\lambda}(\phi^*\phi_{,\lambda} - \phi^*_{,\lambda}\phi) \tag{2.51}$$

that of a spinor field:

$$j^\nu = \bar{\psi}\gamma^\nu\psi \tag{2.52}$$

The interaction Lagrangian with an electromagnetic field is:

$$L_{\text{int}} = -e\bar{\psi}\gamma^\nu\psi A_\nu(x)$$

which is to be added to the free electromagnetic and spinor field Lagrangians.

Another non-geometric mapping is the gauge transformation of the second kind:

$$A'^\mu(x) = A^\mu(x) + \frac{\partial\Lambda(x)}{\partial x_\mu}$$

$$\psi'(x) = e^{ie\Lambda(x)}\psi(x)$$

$$\bar{\psi}'(x) = e^{-ie\Lambda(x)}\bar{\psi}(x)$$

where $\Lambda(x)$ is a scalar function, solution of the wave equation $\Box\Lambda = 0$.

Other quantities of the general form of Q where the current is of the form (2.52), are the baryon number B, the lepton numbers L_μ and L_e. They are, perhaps, related to interactions of the corresponding spinors with hypothetical vector fields in the same way as the electric charge is revealed in interaction with the electromagnetic field. The conservation of the baryon number and of the lepton number, although, empirically established, are however not yet fully understood. In quantum theory, these charges Q, B, L_μ, L_e have integral numbers.

2.13 OUTLINE OF THE TRANSITION INTO QUANTUM THEORY

The correspondence principle states that, given a classical theory, its quantum transcription will be achieved by the substitution of (Hermitian) linear operators for (observable) classical variables and of commutators divided by $i\hbar$ for Poisson brackets between such variables:

$$\{A, B\} \to \frac{1}{i\hbar}[A, B] = \frac{1}{i\hbar}(AB - BA).$$

Thus the position coordinates and momenta of particles $A, B, \ldots$ are Hermitian linear operators which satisfy the commutation rules [see (1.18)]:

$$[x_{jA}, x_{kB}] = [p_{jA}, p_{kB}] = 0$$

$$[x_{jA}, p_{kB}] = i\hbar\delta_{jk}\delta_{AB}.$$

The canonical equations of a system of particles, with a Hamiltonian operator $H(x, p)$, are [see (1.17)]:

$$i\hbar\dot{x}_{jA} = [x_{jA}, H], \qquad i\hbar\dot{p}_{jA} = [p_{jA}, H]$$

and the time evolution of a physical variable $F(x, p, t)$ is defined by the equation:

$$\frac{dF}{dt} = \frac{\partial F}{\partial t} + \frac{1}{i\hbar}[F, H]. \tag{2.53}$$

It is to be noted that x and p do not depend explicitly on t.

These equations give the description of our system of point-particles in the Heisenberg picture. The operators are here represented by matrices and one is interested in the search for transformations which will change the Hamiltonian matrix into diagonal form. The diagonal elements of H are the energy eigenvalues of our system, its only possible observable energy values. Operators which commute among themselves can all be diagonalised by a given transformation. The physical definition of the state of a system is given through the maximum number of commuting observables each of which can thus have a given value in the state in question.

Such operators act on a Hilbert space, a vector space with complex numbers as scalars and a scalar product defined by:

$$\langle\Phi|\Psi\rangle = \langle\Psi|\Phi\rangle^*$$

$$\langle\Phi|\sum c_i\Psi_i\rangle = \sum c_i\langle\Phi|\Psi_i\rangle$$

$$\langle\Phi|\Phi\rangle \geqq 0.$$

$\langle\Phi|\Phi\rangle = 0$ implies $|\Phi\rangle = 0$. Such a vector space must be complete: if $|\Psi_i\rangle$, $i = 1, 2, \ldots$, is a Cauchy sequence of state vectors, i.e., such that given $\varepsilon > 0$ there is an integral number n for which

$$(\langle\Psi_i - \Psi_j|\Psi_i - \Psi_j\rangle)^{1/2} < \varepsilon, \qquad i, j \geqq n$$

then the sequence has a limit $|\Psi\rangle$:

$$\lim_{j\to\infty} (\langle \Psi_j - \Psi | \Psi_j - \Psi \rangle)^{1/2} = 0.$$

If instead of the Heisenberg equations (2.53), we regard the time evolution of the system as described by that of a state vector $|\Psi\rangle$, the fundamental equation is the Schrödinger's equation:

$$i\hbar \frac{\partial\, |\Psi\rangle}{\partial t} = H\,|\Psi\rangle.$$

This is the Schrödinger picture according to which the operators do not depend explicitly on time.

Given an operator A of which all the eigenvalues a and eigenfunctions $|a\rangle$ are known:

$$A\,|a\rangle = a\,|a\rangle, \qquad \langle a|a'\rangle = \delta\,(a - a')$$

one may develop $|\Psi\rangle$ into this complete set of eigenfunctions:

$$|\Psi\rangle = \int da \psi\,(a, t)\,|a\rangle$$

where

$$\psi\,(a, t) = \langle a|\Psi\rangle.$$

The Schrödinger equation will read in this case, in terms of the amplitudes $\psi\,(a, t)$:

$$i\hbar\,\frac{\partial\psi\,(a, t)}{\partial t} = \int db\,\langle a|H|b\rangle\,\psi\,(b, t).$$

The usual formulation of one-particle quantum mechanics in x-space is based on the equation:

$$i\hbar\,\frac{\partial}{\partial t}\,\psi\,(\mathbf{x}, t) = \int d^3y\,\langle \mathbf{x}|H|y\rangle\,\psi\,(\mathbf{y}, t)$$

where, for local potentials:

$$\langle \mathbf{x}|H|\mathbf{y}\rangle = H(\mathbf{y})\,\delta\,(\mathbf{x} - \mathbf{y}).$$

Our system may, however, be more complicated. In the case of a system of photons, this will be described in the Heisenberg picture by operators $A^\mu(x)$ such that [see (2.30)]:

$$[A^\mu\,(\mathbf{x}, t), A^\lambda\,(\mathbf{y}, t)] = [\pi_\mu\,(\mathbf{x}, t), \pi_\lambda\,(\mathbf{y}, t)] = 0$$
$$[A^\mu\,(\mathbf{x}, t), \pi_\lambda\,(\mathbf{y}, t)] = i\hbar\delta^\mu_\lambda\delta\,(\mathbf{x} - \mathbf{y}) \qquad (2.54)$$

and the free-field covariant commutation rules are (see [2.35]):

$$[A^\mu(x), A^\lambda(y)] = i\hbar c g^{\mu\lambda} D(x - y). \qquad (2.54a)$$

The Lorentz supplementary condition, however, cannot be transcribed in a simple way into quantum theory. If the operator relation $(\partial A^\mu/\partial x^\mu) = 0$ were true, one would have $(\partial \pi^\lambda/\partial x^\lambda) = 0$ and this would be in conflict with the commutators (2.54; 2.54a). The correct transcription of the Lorentz supplementary condition in quantum electrodynamics is to consider the positive frequency part, $A^{\mu(+)}$ of A^μ, according to the Fourier representation (λ is the polarisation):

$$A^\mu(x) = \frac{1}{(2\pi)^{3/2}} \int \frac{d^3k}{(2k^0)^{1/2}} \sum_\lambda e^\mu(\lambda, \mathbf{k}) \left[a(\lambda, \mathbf{k}) e^{-ikx} + a^\dagger(\lambda, \mathbf{k}) e^{ikx}\right]$$

$$= A^{\mu(+)} + A^{\mu(-)}$$

and select those state vectors $|\Psi\rangle$ restricted by the condition:

$$\frac{\partial A^{\mu(+)}}{\partial x^\mu} |\Psi\rangle = 0.$$

Another example of a quantum system is a pion in interaction with a photon. As pions have a strong interaction with nucleons, the Lagrangian of pions and photons must include the terms relative to the nucleon's field. The corresponding Lagrangian is thus (weak interactions being neglected):

$$L = L_\pi + L_N + L_{\text{rad}} + L_{\text{int}} \qquad (2.55)$$

where:

$$L_\pi = \tfrac{1}{2}(\mu^2 \phi_j^2 - g^{\alpha\beta} \phi_{j,\alpha} \phi_{j,\beta})$$

is the free pion-field Lagrangian described by three real (Hermitian) fields ϕ_j, $j = 1, 2, 3$;

$$L_N = \frac{i}{2}\left(\bar{\psi}_N \gamma^\mu \frac{\partial \psi_N}{\partial x^\mu} - \frac{\partial \bar{\psi}_N}{\partial x^\mu} \gamma^\mu \psi_N\right) - K \bar{\psi}_N \psi_N$$

is the free nucleon-field Lagrangian where:

$$\psi_N = \begin{pmatrix} \psi_p \\ \psi_n \end{pmatrix}.$$

ψ_p and ψ_n are the four-component spinors of the proton and neutron respectively; L_{rad} is given by (2.48) with $K = 0$ and $\phi^\mu = A^\mu$:

$$L_{\text{int}} = g\bar{\psi}_N\gamma^5\tau_j\psi_N\phi_j + e\bar{\psi}_N\gamma_\mu \frac{1 + \tau_3}{2} \psi_N A^\mu + e j^\pi_\mu A^\mu$$

comprises the nucleon–pion interactions, with:

$$\tau_1 = \begin{pmatrix} 0 & 1 \\ 1 & 0 \end{pmatrix}, \quad \tau_2 = \begin{pmatrix} 0 & -i \\ i & 0 \end{pmatrix}, \quad \tau_3 = \begin{pmatrix} 1 & 0 \\ 0 & -1 \end{pmatrix}$$

the nucleon–photon interaction and the pion–photon interaction where j^π_μ is given in equations (2.51) and (2.47). The total electric current of this system which obeys Noether's theorem, is:

$$j^\mu = ig^{\mu\lambda}(\phi^*\phi_{,\lambda} - \phi^*_{,\lambda}\phi) + \bar{\psi}_N\gamma^\mu \frac{1 + \tau_3}{2} \psi_N. \tag{2.56}$$

The nucleon field—all spin $\frac{1}{2}$ fields—is however quantized according to anticommutators, as required by the exclusion principle.

2.14 CONSERVED CURRENT AND EQUALITY OF CHARGES OF ELEMENTARY PARTICLES

An illustration of the importance of conserved Noether's quantities is furnished by the relationship between conserved current and the equality of charges of elementary particles. The charge of an electron is revealed by its interaction with a photon. If weak interactions are neglected, the electron charge is given by the matrix element:

$$Q_e = \int \langle e_{\text{out}}|\psi^\dagger\psi|e_{\text{in}}\rangle \, d^3x$$

where $|e_{\text{in}}\rangle$ and $|e_{\text{out}}\rangle$ are the incident and outgoing electron in interaction with a photon:

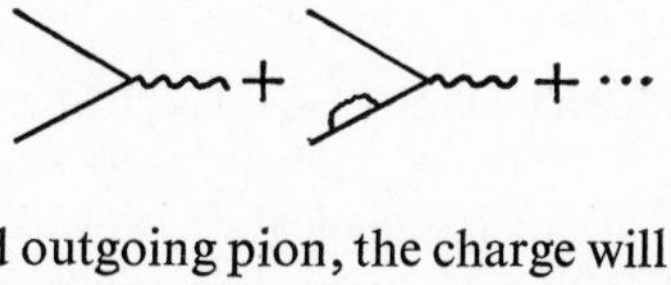

For an incoming and outgoing pion, the charge will be:

$$Q_\pi = \int \langle \pi_{\text{out}}|j^\pi_0|\pi_{\text{in}}\rangle \, d^3x + \int \langle \pi_{\text{out}}|\psi^\dagger_N\psi_N|\pi_{\text{in}}\rangle \, d^3x.$$

The first term is of the type of the above one and we may assume equal to it, the second term might give additional contributions and make $Q_\pi \neq Q_e$, as illustrated by graphs such as the following one:

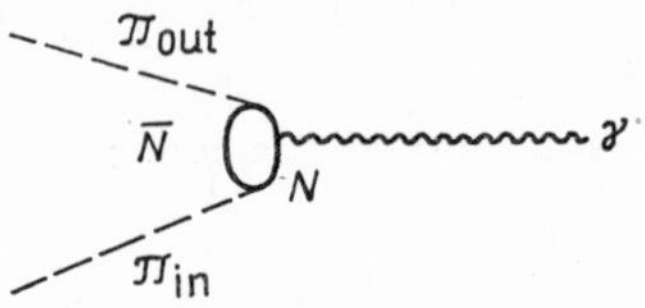

However, the solutions ψ_N and ϕ to the equations derived from the Lagrangian (2.55) must be such that in the remote past they describe free nucleons and pions:

$$\lim_{t\to-\infty} (\Box + \mu^2)\phi = 0$$

$$\lim_{t\to-\infty} \left(i\gamma^\lambda \frac{\partial \psi_N}{\partial x^\lambda} - K\psi_N \right) = 0.$$

Therefore, in the remote past, $\int \psi_N^\dagger \psi_N \, d^3x$ = number of nucleons − number of antinucleons; since there is only one pion in the distant past one has:

$$\lim_{t\to-\infty} \langle \pi_{\text{out}} | \int \psi_N^\dagger \psi_N \, d^3x | \pi_{\text{in}} \rangle = 0$$

and

$$\lim_{t\to-\infty} Q_\pi(t) = \langle \pi_{\text{out}} | \int j_0^\pi d^3x | \pi_{\text{in}} \rangle = Q_\pi^0$$

which we assume equal to the electron's charge.

In view of the total current conservation, (2.56), one has:

$$\frac{dQ_\pi(t)}{dt} = 0$$

hence $Q_\pi = Q_\pi^0 = Q_e$.

2.15 SYMMETRY OPERATIONS IN QUANTUM THEORY

To canonical transformations in classical physics, there correspond unitary transformations in quantum theory: given a state vector $|\Psi\rangle$, one can define a new state vector $|\Psi'\rangle$ after the physical variables of the system have undergone a certain transformation. It is postulated that there exists a linear operator U which transforms $|\Psi\rangle$ into $|\Psi'\rangle$

$$|\Psi'\rangle = U|\Psi\rangle .$$

The transformation U in Hilbert space is a *symmetry operation* if the physical laws obtained from $|\Psi'\rangle$ are the same as those obtained from $|\Psi\rangle$. Let R be the transformation of physical variables which induces the mapping U of the Hilbert space into itself. We shall write $U = U(R)$. If the set of all possible transformations R forms a group, the set of operations $U(R)$ will also form a group—and is called a representation (an infinite dimensional one)—of $\{R\}$ if:

(a) the unity in Hilbert space corresponds to the unity in the set $\{R\}$;

(b) to the product R_2R_1, R_1, $R_2 \in \{R\}$, there corresponds the product $U(R_2)\, U(R_1)$ up to a phase factor $\omega\,(R_2, R_1)$:

$$U(1) = I$$

$$U(R_2)\, U(R_1) = \omega\,(R_2, R_1)\, U\,(R_2R_1) .$$

The symmetry operation U is unitary if one postulates the conservation of the scalar product:

$$\langle\Psi'|\Psi'\rangle = \langle\Psi|U^+U|\Psi\rangle = \langle\Psi|\Psi\rangle \tag{2.57}$$

which implies:

$$U^+U = 1 .$$

The equality $UU^+ = I$ follows from the in variance of the completeness relation:

$$\int da\, |a\rangle\, \langle a| = 1$$

In general, however, what must be postulated is the probability conservation:

$$|\langle\Psi'|\Psi'\rangle|^2 = |\langle\Psi|\Psi\rangle|^2 .$$

U is *unitary* if this is satisfied by the equality of the amplitudes (2.57). The equation (2.58) may, however, be still satisfied if:

$$\langle\Psi'|\Psi'\rangle = \langle\Psi|\Psi\rangle^*$$

in which case U is called *anti-unitary* (this is the case of time reversal; in classical mechanics the corresponding transformation is anti-canonical in the sense that it changes the sign of the Poisson bracket $\{x, p\}$).

How do the operators which describe physical variables transform when $|\Psi\rangle \to |\Psi'\rangle = U|\Psi\rangle$? Two main types of transformations may be defined. The Schrödinger type assumes that the operators $O^{[\alpha]}(x)$ do not change:

$$O^{[\alpha]'}(x) = O^{[\alpha]}(x)$$

$$|\Psi'\rangle_S = U|\Psi\rangle$$

so that:

$$\langle\Psi'|O^{[\alpha]'}(x)|\Psi'\rangle_S = \langle\Psi|U^+ O^{[\alpha]}(x)\, U|\Psi\rangle.$$

The Heisenberg type of transformation assumes invariance of the state vectors:

$$|\Psi'\rangle_H = |\Psi\rangle$$

so that

$$\langle\Psi'|O^{[\alpha]'}(x)|\Psi'\rangle_H = \langle\Psi|O^{[\alpha]'}(x)|\Psi\rangle$$

The equivalence between both types of transformation is assured by the equality:

$$\langle\Psi'|O^{[\alpha]'}(x)|\Psi'\rangle_H = \langle\Psi'|O^{[\alpha]'}(x)|\Psi'\rangle_S$$

hence:

$$\langle\Psi|O^{[\alpha]'}(x)|\Psi\rangle = \langle\Psi|U^+ O^{[\alpha]}(x)\, U|\Psi\rangle.$$

The operators transform therefore in the following way:

$$O^{[\alpha]'}(x) = U^+ O^{[\alpha]}(x)\, U. \tag{2.59}$$

If U is a continuous operator, we shall write, for an infinitesimal transformation with parameters $\omega^{[\alpha]}$ (see section 2.9):

$$U = I - \frac{i}{\hbar} U_{[\nu]}\omega^{[\nu]} \tag{2.60}$$

and shall call the hermitian operators $U_{[\nu]}$ the generators of the group. The equations (2.59) and (2.60) give rise to the equation:

$$\delta O^{[\alpha]}(x) = O^{[\alpha]'}(x) - O^{[\alpha]}(x) = \frac{1}{i\hbar}[O^{[\alpha]}(x), U_{[\nu]}]\,\omega^{[\nu]}$$

which corresponds to the classical relationship (2.33). Therefore, if one sets, as in (2.39):

$$\bar{\delta} O^{[\alpha]}(x) = O^{[\alpha]'}(x') - O^{[\alpha]}(x) = \mathscr{F}^{[\alpha]}_{[\beta]}(x)\,\omega^{[\beta]}$$

one gets:

$$\delta O^{[\alpha]}(x) = [\mathscr{F}^{[\alpha]}_{[\beta]}(x) - O^{[\alpha]}_{,\lambda} f^{\lambda}_{[\beta]}]\, \omega^{[\beta]}$$

hence:

$$\mathscr{F}^{[\alpha]}_{[\beta]}(x) - O^{[\alpha]}_{,\lambda}(x) f^{\lambda}_{[\beta]} = \frac{1}{i\hbar}\, [O^{[\alpha]}(x), U_{[\beta]}]$$

where $f^{[\alpha]}_{[\beta]}$ is given by relation (2.37).

The reader will find the form of these equations corresponding to space–time translation, $U_{[\nu]} \to P_\nu$, to a homogeneous Lorentz transformation, $U_{[\nu]} \to J_{\lambda\nu}$ and to a gauge transformation of the second kind, $U_{[\nu]} \to -Q\sqrt{(\hbar/c)}$. Thus, in an infinitesimal translation along the axis of abcissae by the amount a:

$$x' = x + a \tag{2.61}$$

one should have, according to (2.59) and (2.60):

$$x' = U^+ x U = \left(1 + \frac{i}{\hbar} a p_x\right) x \left(1 - \frac{i}{\hbar} a p_x\right) \tag{2.62}$$

the comparison of (2.61) and (2.62) leads to the commutation relation between x and p_x:

$$[x, p_x] = i\hbar\,.$$

If one performs a rotation by an infinitesimal angle ϕ around the z axis:

$$x' = x - \phi y \qquad y' = y + \phi x \qquad z' = z$$

or

$$\mathbf{x}' = R(\phi)\,\mathbf{x} \qquad R(\phi) = I + \begin{pmatrix} 0 & -\phi & 0 \\ \phi & 0 & 0 \\ 0 & 0 & 0 \end{pmatrix}$$

one must have:

$$x' = U^+ x U = \left(I + \frac{i}{\hbar}\phi L_z\right) x \left(I - \frac{i}{\hbar}\phi L_z\right) = x - \phi y$$

$$y' = U^+ y U = \left(I + \frac{i}{\hbar}\phi L_z\right) y \left(I - \frac{i}{\hbar}\phi L_z\right) = y + \phi x$$

hence

$$[x, L_z] = -i\hbar y$$

$$[y, L_z] = i\hbar x\,.$$

If the rotation is around an axis δ by an angle α, one has:

$$U(\alpha, n) = I - \frac{i}{\hbar}\,\alpha\,(n \cdot L)$$

and the consideration of two successive rotations around two axis in different order gives rise to the angular momentum commutation rules:

$$\mathbf{L} \times \mathbf{L} = i\hbar \mathbf{L} .$$

The equations which connect a field $O^{[\alpha]}(x)$ with its charge Q:

$$\frac{1}{\sqrt{(\hbar c)}}\,[O^{[\alpha]}(x), Q] = O^{[\alpha]}(x)$$

$$\frac{1}{\sqrt{(\hbar c)}}\,[O^{[\alpha]+}(x), Q] = -O^{[\alpha]+}(x)$$

follow from the identification of

$$O^{[\alpha]\prime}(x) = e^{i\varepsilon} O^{[\alpha]}(x) \simeq (1 + i\varepsilon)\, O^{[\alpha]}(x)$$

with:

$$O^{[\alpha]\prime}(x) = U^{+}(\varepsilon)\, O^{[\alpha]}(x)\, U(\varepsilon) = \left(I - \frac{i}{\sqrt{(\hbar c)}}\, Q\varepsilon\right) O^{[\alpha]}(x) \left(I + \frac{i}{\sqrt{(\hbar c)}}\, Q\varepsilon\right).$$

The charge operator is the generator of the gauge group.

CHAPTER 3

The Problem of the Energy-Momentum Tensor Conservation in the Relativistic Theory of Gravitation

3.1 INTRODUCTION

In field theories in a flat space, i.e., in a space with a Lorentz metric tensor (2.10), conserved quantities $S_{[\beta]}(x_0)$ (see parag. 2.H):

$$\frac{dS_{[\beta]}}{dx^0} = 0$$

are those derived from Noether's tensors $N^{\lambda}_{[\beta]}$

$$S_{[\beta]} = \int d\sigma_\lambda \, N^{\lambda}_{[\beta]}(x)$$

which obey the divergence euqation:

$$\frac{\partial N^{\lambda}_{[\beta]}}{\partial x^\lambda} = N^{\lambda}_{[\beta],\lambda} = 0.$$

In the relativistic theory of gravitation, such conservation laws are not covariant. In the presence of a gravitational field, $g^{\mu\nu}(x)$, the covariant divergence of a tensor contains, besides the usual four-divergence, additional terms which depend on the gravitational field derivatives. Einstein's equations are established in such a way that the covariant divergence of the energy–momentum tensor—the source of the field—vanish, as a generalisation of the equation (2.41a) for this tensor. It follows from this that one cannot build up a conserved energy–momentum vector.

In this section, we shall present a brief review of Einstein's theory and then examine, in a simple fashion, this question. It will be seen that objects can be constructed which are conserved but these objects are not tensors nor unique.

3.2 THE SEARCH FOR RELATIVISTIC GRAVITATIONAL FIELD EQUATIONS

The starting point of a relativistic theory of gravitation is the search for covariant equations which generalise Poisson's equation for the Newton gravitational field $V(\mathbf{x})$:

$$\nabla^2 V(\mathbf{x}) = -G\varrho_m(\mathbf{x}). \tag{3.1}$$

G is the gravitational coupling constant, $\varrho_m(\mathbf{x})$ is the mass density, source of V. This may be regarded as the static limit of the equation:

$$\Box V(x) = G\varrho_m(x) \tag{3.2}$$

where $\Box$ is the D'Alembertian operator (2.24a) and $x = (x^0, \mathbf{x})$. Now, however, unlike the electric charge, the mass is not Lorentz invariant and thus $\varrho_m(x)$ cannot be regarded as the time component of a four-vector. In view of the equivalence between mass and energy, we see from equations (2.42a) and (2.42b) that the mass density is the zero–zero component of the energy momentum tensor. The problem reduces then to find, from simple arguments, a tensor $B_{\mu\nu}$ which can be a function of the gravitational field and its first and second derivatives, and equate it to $f \cdot T_{\mu\nu}$:

$$B_{\mu\nu}(x) = fT_{\mu\nu}(x) \tag{3.3}$$

where f is a coupling constant. The equation (3.3) must go over into equation (3.2) in the approximation for weak fields.

Einstein's beautiful theory of gravitation identifies this field with the metric of the Riemannian space–time geometry. In its construction, Einstein was intuitively guided by two principles:

(a) the equivalence principle,

(2) the postulate of covariance of natural laws (not only under the Poincaré transformation group but) under continuous one-to-one coordinate transformations:

$$x'^{\mu} = f^{\mu}(x, x^1, x^2, x^3) \qquad \mu = 0, 1, 2, 3 \tag{3.4}$$

with continuous first derivatives $\partial x'^{\mu}/\partial x^{\lambda}$ and non-vanishing Jacobian.

The so-called apparent forces are those—like the inertial, centrifugal and Coriolis forces—which are proportional to inertial mass and which can be transformed away by a proper choice of the coordinate system. Thus, as well known, if the equations of a point-particle have the form:

$$m\ddot{\mathbf{x}} = \mathbf{F} \tag{3.5}$$

in an inertial frame S, the transition into a frame S' which rotates around the z-axis of S with constant angular velocity ω:

$$\begin{aligned} x' &= x \cos \omega t + y \sin \omega t \\ y' &= -x \sin \omega t + y \cos \omega t \\ z' &= z \end{aligned} \tag{3.6}$$

or

$$\begin{aligned} x &= x' \cos \omega t - y' \sin \omega t \\ y &= x' \sin \omega t + y' \cos \omega t \end{aligned}$$

leads equations (3.5) into assuming the form:

$$\begin{aligned} m(\ddot{x}' - 2\omega\dot{y}' - \omega^2 x') &= F'_x \\ m(\ddot{y}' + 2\omega\dot{x}' + \omega^2 y') &= F'_y \\ m\ddot{z}' &= F'_z \end{aligned} \tag{3.7}$$

where

$$\begin{aligned} F'_x &= F_x \cos \omega t + F_y \sin \omega t \\ F'_y &= -F_x \sin \omega t + F_y \cos \omega t \\ F'_z &= F_z \end{aligned}$$

The terms proportional to $\dot{\mathbf{x}}'$—the Coriolis force—and to $\mathbf{x}'$—the centrifugal force—can thus be transformed away by a proper choice of the coordinate system, namely S.

Now the famous Einstein's elevator experiment led him to state that the gravitational force, is at least locally, equivalent to an accelerated reference frame and can, therefore, be regarded as an apparent force. The elevator experiment is this: an observer enclosed in a box verifies that all objects inside the box have a downward acceleration, independent of their mass. His interpretation of this fact is either (a) that there is a source of a gravitational field at the bottom, which attracts all objects and communicates them the observed acceleration; or (b) that the box is accelerated upwards and the inertia of all objects inside it gives them the observed downward acceleration. The two interpretations are equivalent because the inertial mass of any body is equal to its gravitational mass, as has been found experimentally. Einstein postulated this equality and the full equivalence between a homogeneous gravitational field and an accelerated frame of reference. This equivalence principle has the immediate consequence that any energy signal, such as a light ray, travelling across a gravitational field, is deflected by it.

Now, the space–time interval ds^2, which in an inertial frame has the form

$$ds^2 = (dx^0)^2 - (d\mathbf{x})^2 = g^{(0)}_{\mu\nu}\, dx^\mu\, dx^\nu \tag{3.8}$$

where $g^{(0)}_{\mu\nu}$ is the Lorentz metric tensor (2.10), vests the more general form:

$$ds^2 = g_{\mu\nu}(x)\, dx^\mu\, dx^\nu \qquad g_{\mu\nu}(x) = g_{\nu\mu}(x) \tag{3.9}$$

when it refers to a non-inertial frame of reference. Thus in the case of the rotation (3.6), one has:

$$ds^2 = \left[1 - \frac{\omega^2}{c^2}(x'^2 + y'^2)\right](dx^0)^2 - (d\mathbf{x}')^2 - 2\frac{\omega}{c}[y'\, dx' + x'\, dy']\, dx^0.$$

The heuristic considerations of the equivalence principle led Einstein to *postulate* that the metric tensor $g_{\mu\nu}(x)$ is identical with the gravitational field and that the description of all physical processes produced by this field is to be given by the Riemannian geometry of the four-dimensional space–time continuum. This is the essential postulate in Einstein's theory. As the equation of motion in any theory can be manipulated into a covariant form, it is the dynamical meaning of $g_{\mu\nu}(x)$ which is important and shows that the postulated invariance of natural laws with respect to general coordinate transformations is a dynamical—not geometric—invariance (see Fock[7]).

In the sections 3.3–3.9 the principal notions involved in the establishment of Einstein's gravitational field equations will be briefly recalled.

3.3 TENSORS IN A RIEMANNIAN SPACE

Let us then consider a four-dimensional space in which the neighborhood of each point x has an interval defined by the Riemannian metric of the form (3.9); the transformation laws (3.4) and their inverse establish a one-to-one correspondence between two different maps of each of these regions.

A *contravariant vector* $F^\alpha(x)$ is a set of four functions associated to each such point which transforms, under the correspondence (3.4) as:

$$F'^\mu(x') = \frac{\partial x'^\mu}{\partial x^\beta} F^\beta(x) \tag{3.10}$$

where the sum over repeated indices is, as before, understood, and $\partial x'^\alpha/\partial x^\beta$ are the derivatives of the functions (3.4). The law (3.10) is a natural extension of the transformation law for coordinate differentials:

$$dx'^\alpha = \frac{\partial x'^\alpha}{\partial x^\beta} dx^\beta$$

which are linear in the dx^β.

The notion of *covariant vector* results from the differentiation of an invariant function:

$$\phi'(x') = \phi(x).$$

One has:

$$\frac{\partial \phi'(x')}{\partial x'^\alpha} = \frac{\partial \phi(x)}{\partial x^\beta} \frac{\partial x^\beta}{\partial x'^\alpha}.$$

The derivatives $\partial\phi(x)/\partial x^\beta$ are said to form a covariant vector. This entity is, in general, a set $K_\alpha(x)$ such that, under the transformations (3.4), transform as:

$$K'_\alpha(x') = K_\beta(x) \frac{\partial x^\beta}{\partial x'^\alpha}. \tag{3.11}$$

In general, a *tensor* with contravariant and covariant indices, $T^{\mu\nu\cdots}_{\alpha\beta\cdots}(x)$, is defined by the equations:

$$T'^{\mu'\nu'\cdots}_{\alpha'\beta'\cdots}(x') = \frac{\partial x'^{\mu'}}{\partial x^\mu} \frac{\partial x'^{\nu'}}{\partial x^\nu} \cdots T^{\mu\nu\cdots}_{\alpha\beta\cdots}(x) \frac{\partial x^\alpha}{\partial x'^{\alpha'}} \frac{\partial x^\beta}{\partial x'^{\beta'}} \cdots \tag{3.12}$$

which is an extension of the transformation of direct products of vectors:

$$A^\mu(x)\, A^\nu(x) \ldots B_\alpha(x)\, B_\beta(x) \ldots$$

A *tensor density* of weight n transforms like (3.12) with an extra-factor J^n on the right-hand side, where J is the Jacobian of the mappings (3.4).

A contraction of a tensor with μ upper indices and l lower indices is the sum over one lower and one upper indice and it is another tensor with $\mu - 1$ upper and $l - 1$ lower indices. The scalar product of two vectors is the contraction of their one-upper-one-lower index tensor product and is invariant:

$$A'^{\mu'}(x')\,B'_{\mu'}(x') = \frac{\partial x'^{\mu'}}{\partial x^{\mu}}\,A^{\mu}(x)\,B_{\alpha}(x)\,\frac{\partial x^{\alpha}}{\partial x'^{\mu'}} = \delta^{\alpha}_{\mu}A^{\mu}(x)\,B_{\alpha}(x) = A^{\mu}(x)\,B_{\mu}(x).$$

δ^{μ}_{ν} is a tensor:

$$\delta'^{\mu'}_{\alpha'} \equiv \frac{\partial x'^{\mu'}}{\partial x'^{\alpha'}} = \frac{\partial x'^{\mu'}}{\partial x^{\mu}}\,\delta^{\mu}_{\alpha}\,\frac{\partial x^{\alpha}}{\partial x'^{\alpha'}}$$

The symmetry properties of tensors refer only to indices of the same floor and are invariant with respect to (3.4).

3.4 PARALLEL DISPLACEMENT

An immediate consequence of the definitions (3.10), (3.11) is that the derivative of a vector (tensor) is not a tensor (of higher rank), except if the transformations (3.4) are linear (Lorentz metric). Indeed, according to (3.10):

$$\frac{\partial F'^{\mu}(x')}{\partial x'^{\alpha}} = \frac{\partial}{\partial x'^{\alpha}}\left[\frac{\partial x'^{\mu}}{\partial x^{\beta}}\,F^{\beta}(x)\right] = \frac{\partial}{\partial x^{\lambda}}\left[\frac{\partial x'^{\mu}}{\partial x^{\beta}}\,F^{\beta}(x)\right]\frac{\partial x^{\lambda}}{\partial x'^{\alpha}}$$

$$= \frac{\partial x'^{\mu}}{\partial x^{\beta}}\,\frac{\partial F^{\beta}}{\partial x^{\lambda}}\,\frac{\partial x^{\lambda}}{\partial x'^{\alpha}} + \frac{\partial x^{\lambda}}{\partial x'^{\alpha}}\,F^{\beta}(x)\,\frac{\partial^2 x'^{\mu}}{\partial x^{\lambda}\partial x^{\beta}} \qquad (3.13)$$

The last term is the obstacle for the derivative of $F^{\mu}(x)$ being a tensor—it vanishes when the transformations (3.4) are linear.

It is an essential assumption in what follows that *it is always possible to find, in every point of space–time, a frame referred to which the neighborhood of this point is describable by the Lorentz* (Minkowskian) *geometry*. In such a locally inertial frame, the parallel displacement of a vector to another point of the neighborhood does not change the vector components and the scalar product of this vector and any other is invariant.

For a general reference frame, the notion of parallel displacement of a vector $F^{\alpha}(x)$ from the point $M(x)$ to another of its neighborhood, $M'\,(x + dx)$, must leave the scalar product of F^{α} with an arbitrary vector, invariant. If δF^{α} is the change in F^{α} due to such a parallel displacement, we shall set it as a bilinear function of $F^{\alpha}(x)$ and dx^{α}:

$$\delta F^{\mu}(x) = -\Gamma^{\mu}_{\alpha\beta}(x)\,F^{\alpha}(x)\,dx^{\beta}. \qquad (3.14)$$

The Γ's are called Christoffel symbols. It can be shown that they are symmetric i.e., that in every point of the space-time continuum they can be made to obey the equality:

$$\Gamma^{\mu}_{\alpha\beta} = \Gamma^{\mu}_{\beta\alpha}. \tag{3.15}$$

The proof can be given by choosing dx^{μ} as the vector F^{μ} and by choosing new coordinates x'^{μ} locally Minkowskian:

$$\delta\,(dx'^{\alpha}) = 0. \tag{3.16}$$

In fact, in view of this choice and of the definition:

$$dx^{\mu} = \frac{\partial x^{\mu}}{\partial x'^{\nu}}\, dx'^{\nu}$$

one obtains:

$$\delta\,(dx^{\mu}) = \frac{\partial^2 x^{\mu}}{\partial x'^{\nu} \partial x'^{\lambda}} \frac{\partial x'^{\nu}}{\partial x^{\alpha}} \frac{\partial x'^{\lambda}}{\partial x^{\beta}}\, dx^{\alpha} dx^{\beta}$$

which, compared with

$$\delta\,(dx^{\mu}) = -\Gamma^{\mu}_{\alpha\beta}\, dx^{\alpha}\, dx^{\beta}$$

gives

$$\Gamma^{\mu}_{\alpha\beta}(x) = -\frac{\partial^2 x^{\mu}}{\partial x'^{\nu} \partial x'^{\lambda}} \frac{\partial x'^{\nu}}{\partial x^{\alpha}} \frac{\partial x'^{\lambda}}{\partial x^{\beta}}$$

which makes the equality (3.15) obvious. The essential point here is that the choice of locally Minkowskian frame is possible everywhere and that the equality (3.15) can thus always be satisfied.

The Christoffel symbols—which, as it will be shown, do not form a tensor—define an *affine connection* around the point x.

Given the metric tensor $g_{\alpha\beta}(x)$ (and the reader will easily show that this is indeed a tensor), one can associate a contravariant tensor $g^{\mu\nu}(x)$ such that for all x:

$$g^{\mu\nu}(x)\, g_{\nu\alpha}(x) = \delta^{\mu}_{\alpha}. \tag{3.17}$$

Its components are given by:

$$g^{\mu\nu}(x) = \frac{\Delta^{\mu\nu}}{g} \tag{3.18}$$

where g is the determinant of the $g_{\alpha\beta}$'s and $\Delta^{\alpha\beta}$ is the cofactor of element $g_{\alpha\beta}$. The development of g according to the element of a line α_0:

$$g = \sum_{\beta} g_{\alpha_0\beta} \Delta^{\alpha_0\beta}$$

gives

$$\frac{\partial g}{\partial g_{\alpha\beta}} = \Delta^{\alpha\beta}$$

since $\Delta_{\alpha_0\beta}$ does not contain $g_{\alpha_0\beta}$. Therefore:

$$g^{\mu\nu}(x) = \frac{1}{g}\frac{\partial g}{\partial g_{\mu\nu}}.$$

From these relations and (3.17) one obtains:

$$dg = \frac{\partial g}{\partial g_{\mu\nu}} dg_{\mu\nu} = \Delta^{\mu\nu}\, dg_{\mu\nu} = gg^{\mu\nu}\, dg_{\mu\nu} = -gg_{\mu\nu}\, dg^{\mu\nu}$$

$$\frac{\partial g}{\partial x^\alpha} = gg^{\mu\nu}\frac{\partial g_{\mu\nu}}{\partial x^\alpha} = -gg_{\mu\nu}\frac{\partial g^{\mu\nu}}{\partial x^\alpha}. \tag{3.19}$$

The tensors $g_{\mu\nu}$ and $g^{\mu\nu}$ are instrumental in the transition between contravariant and covariant vectors:

$$F^\mu(x) = g^{\mu\nu}(x)\, F_\nu(x)$$
$$F_\alpha(x) = g_{\alpha\beta}(x)\, F^\beta(x)$$

and for the raising and lowering of indices.

3.5 TRANSFORMATION LAWS OF THE CHRISTOFFEL SYMBOLS

The Christoffel symbols can be expressed in terms of the metric tensor and its first derivatives. By definition, given a vector $F^\mu(x)$, the parallel displacement is such that:

$$\delta\,(F^\alpha(x)\, F_\alpha(x)) = 0$$

and this means that the following equation holds:

$$g_{\alpha\beta}\,(x + dx)\,\bar{F}^\alpha\,(x + dx)\,\bar{F}^\beta\,(x + dx) - g_{\alpha\beta}(x)\, F^\alpha(x)\, F^\beta(x) = 0$$

where $\bar{F}^\alpha\,(x + dx)$ is the vector obtained from $F^\alpha(x)$ by parallel displacement along dx^λ:

$$\bar{F}^\alpha\,(x + dx) = F^\alpha(x) - \Gamma^\alpha_{\mu\nu} F^\mu(x)\, dx^\nu.$$

From this relation and from (up to terms in dx):

$$g_{\alpha\beta}\,(x + dx) = g_{\alpha\beta}(x) + \frac{\partial g_{\alpha\beta}}{\partial x^\lambda}\, dx^\lambda$$

one gets:

$$\frac{\partial g_{\alpha\beta}}{\partial x^\lambda} - g_{\alpha\eta}\Gamma^\eta_{\beta\lambda} - g_{\eta\beta}\Gamma^\eta_{\alpha\lambda} = 0\,. \tag{3.20}$$

Let us use the symmetry of the Γ's with respect to their lower indices. We have (interchange α and λ then β and λ):

$$\frac{\partial g_{\lambda\beta}}{\partial x^\alpha} - g_{\lambda\eta}\Gamma^\eta_{\beta\alpha} - g_{\eta\beta}\Gamma^\eta_{\alpha\lambda} = 0$$

$$\frac{\partial g_{\alpha\lambda}}{\partial x^\beta} - g_{\alpha\eta}\Gamma^\eta_{\beta\lambda} - g_{\eta\lambda}\Gamma^\eta_{\alpha\beta} = 0\,.$$

The sum of the last two equations gives:

$$\frac{\partial g_{\lambda\beta}}{\partial x^\alpha} + \frac{\partial g_{\alpha\lambda}}{\partial x^\beta} - g_{\alpha\eta}\Gamma^\eta_{\beta\lambda} - g_{\beta\eta}\Gamma^\eta_{\alpha\lambda} - 2g_{\lambda\eta}\Gamma^\eta_{\alpha\beta} = 0$$

whence, in view of (3.20):

$$\frac{\partial g_{\lambda\beta}}{\partial x^\alpha} + \frac{\partial g_{\alpha\lambda}}{\partial x^\beta} - \frac{\partial g_{\alpha\beta}}{\partial x^\lambda} - 2g_{\lambda\eta}\Gamma^\eta_{\alpha\beta} = 0\,.$$

Therefore (see (3.17)):

$$\Gamma^\nu_{\alpha\beta}(x) = \frac{1}{2}\, g^{\nu\lambda}(x)\left(\frac{\partial g_{\lambda\beta}}{\partial x^\alpha} + \frac{\partial g_{\alpha\lambda}}{\partial x^\beta} - \frac{\partial g_{\alpha\beta}}{\partial x^\lambda}\right) \tag{3.21}$$

which is the searched-for expression of the Christoffel symbols. The corresponding all-lower indices symbols are:

$$\Gamma_{\xi,\alpha\beta} = g_{\xi\nu}\Gamma^\nu_{\alpha\beta} = \frac{1}{2}\left(\frac{\partial g_{\xi\beta}}{\partial x^\alpha} + \frac{\partial g_{\alpha\xi}}{\partial x^\beta} - \frac{\partial g_{\alpha\beta}}{\partial x^\xi}\right). \tag{3.22}$$

From these expressions and from the transformation laws of the tensors $g_{\alpha\beta}$, the reader will be able to obtain the transformation formulae for the Γ's

$$\Gamma'^\nu_{\alpha\beta}(x') = \frac{\partial x'^\nu}{\partial x^\lambda}\,\Gamma^\lambda_{\eta\varepsilon}(x)\,\frac{\partial x^\eta \partial x^\varepsilon}{\partial x'^\alpha \partial x'^\beta} - \frac{\partial^2 x'^\nu}{\partial x^\eta \partial x^\varepsilon}\,\frac{\partial x^\eta}{\partial x'^\alpha}\,\frac{\partial x^\varepsilon}{\partial x'^\beta}\,. \tag{3.23}$$

The Christoffel symbols—because of the last term at the right-hand side—*are not a tensor.*

If the tensor vanishes at a point in a given coordinate system, it will clearly vanish at the transformed point in all coordinate systems. For the Christoffel symbols, on the contrary, it is always possible to choose a coordinate system (up to a linear transformation) referred to which $\Gamma^{\nu}_{\alpha\beta}$ vanishes locally. Indeed, let x_0^{μ} be a point in a given frame for which $\Gamma^{\nu}_{\alpha\beta}(x_0) \neq 0$. If one carries out the following transformation:

$$x'^{\nu} = x^{\nu} - x_0^{\nu} + \tfrac{1}{2}\Gamma^{\nu}_{\eta\varepsilon}(x_0)\,(x^{\eta} - x_0^{\eta})\,(x^{\varepsilon} - x_0^{\varepsilon})$$

one gets:

$$\frac{\partial x'^{\nu}}{\partial x^{\lambda}} = \delta^{\nu}_{\lambda} + \Gamma^{\nu}_{\lambda\varepsilon}(x_0)\,(x^{\varepsilon} - x_0^{\varepsilon}) \qquad \delta^{\nu}_{\lambda} = \frac{\partial x^{\nu}}{\partial x'^{\lambda}} + \Gamma^{\nu}_{\eta\varepsilon}(x_0)\,(x^{\eta} - x_0^{\eta})\,\frac{\partial x^{\varepsilon}}{\partial x'^{\lambda}}$$

and

$$\frac{\partial^2 x'^{\nu}}{\partial x^{\eta}\,\partial x^{\varepsilon}} = \Gamma^{\nu}_{\eta\varepsilon}(x_0)$$

therefore, since:

$$\left(\frac{\partial x'^{\nu}}{\partial x^{\lambda}}\right)_0 = \delta^{\nu}_{\lambda}\,; \qquad \left(\frac{\partial x^{\eta}}{\partial x'^{\alpha}}\right)_0 = \delta^{\eta}_{\alpha}$$

the transformed of $\Gamma^{\nu}_{\alpha\beta}(x_0)$, according to (3.23) is:

$$\Gamma'^{\nu}_{\alpha\beta} = \delta^{\nu}_{\lambda}\Gamma^{\lambda}_{\eta\varepsilon}(x_0)\,\delta^{\eta}_{\alpha}\delta^{\varepsilon}_{\beta} - \Gamma^{\nu}_{\eta\varepsilon}(x_0)\,\delta^{\eta}_{\alpha}\delta^{\varepsilon}_{\beta} = 0\,. \tag{3.23a}$$

What is the meaning of this system, the so-called *geodesic system*?

In a Riemannian space it is natural to define a geodesic line as the one for which the variation of the arc length between two points vanishes:

$$\delta \int_{s_0}^{s_1} \left(g_{\mu\nu}(z)\,\frac{dz^{\mu}}{ds}\,\frac{dz^{\nu}}{ds}\right)^{1/2} ds = 0$$

where s is the parameter of the curve $z^{\mu} = z^{\mu}(s)$.

The equation thus obtained is:

$$\frac{du^{\mu}}{ds} + \Gamma^{\mu}_{\alpha\beta}(z)\,u^{\alpha}u^{\beta} = 0$$

where $u^{\alpha} = (dz^{\alpha}/ds)$. Einstein interpreted this as the equation of a particle in a gravitational field; the particle thus describes a geodesic in space–time the structure of which is Riemannian, due to this field. Therefore the force acting on the particle is $-m_0c^2\Gamma^{\mu}_{\alpha\beta}(z)\,u^{\alpha}u^{\beta}$. The local vanishing of Γ in the geodesic system means that one changes into a new frame (the free-falling Einstein's elevator) within which the gravitational force has been locally transformed away. Only if the gravitational field is uniform can it be transformed away completely. In general, it will only be possible to transform it away in the neighborhood of a point in space-tine.

3.6 COVARIANT DERIVATIVES

Let $F^\alpha(x)$ be a vector field. At a neighboring point $x + dx$, this vector will be:

$$F^\alpha(x + dx) = F^\alpha(x) + dF^\alpha(x). \tag{3.24}$$

At this point the vector obtained by parallel displacement of Γ^α from the point x is:

$$\bar{F}^\alpha(x + \mathrm{d}x) = F^\alpha(x) - \Gamma^\alpha_{\mu\nu\nu} F^\mu(x)\, \mathrm{d}x^\nu \tag{3.24a}$$

The difference between the two vectors (3.24) and (3.24a) is again a vector since they are taken at the same point.

$$F^\alpha(x + dx) - \bar{F}^\alpha(x + dx) = dF^\alpha(x) + \Gamma^\alpha_{\mu\nu}(x)\, F^\mu(x)\, dx^\nu$$

$$= \left(\frac{\partial F^\alpha}{\partial x^\nu} + \Gamma^\alpha_{\mu\nu} F^\mu\right) dx^\nu.$$

The covariant derivative of a vector, by definition

$$F^\alpha_{;\lambda} = F^\alpha_{,\lambda} + \Gamma^\alpha_{\mu\lambda} F^\mu \tag{3.25}$$

is a tensor.

From the observation that the scalar product $F^\alpha(x)\, G_\alpha(x)$ is a scalar and that, therefore, its derivatives form a vector $A_\lambda(x)$:

$$A_\lambda(x) = F^\alpha_{,\lambda}(x)\, G_\alpha(x) + F^\alpha(x)\, G_{\alpha,\lambda}(x)$$

one obtains the new vector:

$$A_\lambda(x) - F^\alpha_{;\lambda}(x)\, G_\alpha(x) = F^\mu(x)\, [G_{\mu,\lambda}(x) - \Gamma^\alpha_{\mu\lambda}(x)\, G_\alpha(x)]$$

hence the covariant derivative of a covariant vector is the tensor:

$$G_{\mu;\lambda}(x) = G_{\mu,\lambda}(x) - \Gamma^\alpha_{\mu\lambda}(x)\, G_\alpha(x).$$

Again, given a second-rank covariant tensor $T_{\alpha\beta}(x)$ and two arbitrary vectors $A^\alpha(x)$, $B^\beta(x)$, at the same point, the product $T_{\alpha\beta}(x)\, A^\alpha(x)\, B^\beta(x)$ is a scalar, therefore:

$$\delta\, (T_{\alpha\beta}(x)\, A^\alpha(x)\, B^\beta(x)) = 0$$

whence, since A^α and B^β are arbitrary, in view of (3.14):

$$\delta T_{\alpha\beta}(x) = (\Gamma^{\lambda}_{\alpha\eta} T_{\lambda\beta} + \Gamma^{\lambda}_{\beta\eta} T_{\alpha\lambda})\, dx^\eta .$$

Now the difference between the two tensors:

$$T_{\alpha\beta}(x + dx) - \bar{T}_{\alpha\beta}(x + dx) = dT_{\alpha\beta}(x) - \delta T_{\alpha\beta}(x)$$

is again a tensor. The corresponding covariant derivative is thus:

$$T_{\alpha\beta;\eta} = T_{\alpha\beta;\eta} - \Gamma^{\lambda}_{\alpha\eta} T_{\lambda\beta} - \Gamma^{\lambda}_{\beta u} T_{\alpha\lambda} .$$

By similar procedures one finds:

$$T^{\alpha\beta}_{;\eta} = T^{\alpha\beta}_{,\eta} + \Gamma^{\alpha}_{\lambda\eta} T^{\lambda\beta} + \Gamma^{\beta}_{\lambda\eta} T^{\alpha\lambda}$$

and, in general:

$$\begin{aligned} T^{\mu\nu\ldots}_{\alpha\beta\ldots;\lambda} = T^{\mu\nu\ldots}_{\alpha\beta\ldots,\lambda} + \Gamma^{\mu}_{a\lambda} T^{a\nu\ldots}_{\alpha\beta\ldots} + \Gamma^{\nu}_{a\lambda} T^{\mu a\ldots}_{\alpha\beta\ldots} + \cdots \\ - \Gamma^{m}_{\alpha\lambda} T^{\mu\nu\ldots}_{m\beta\ldots} - \Gamma^{m}_{\beta\lambda} T^{\mu\nu\ldots}_{\alpha m\ldots} - \cdots \end{aligned} \quad (3.26)$$

The covariant differentiation depends therefore on the rank of the tensor which it is going to be applied to. Thus we can write:

$$F^{\alpha}_{;\lambda} = D^{\alpha}_{m\lambda} F^{m}(x)$$

where

$$D^{\alpha}_{m\lambda} = \frac{\partial}{\partial x^\lambda} \delta^{\alpha}_{m} + \Gamma^{\alpha}_{m\lambda} . \quad (3.27a)$$

Also:

$$T^{\alpha\beta}_{;\lambda} = D^{\alpha\beta}_{mn\lambda} T^{mn}(x)$$

with

$$D^{\alpha\beta}_{mn\lambda} = \frac{\partial}{\partial x^\lambda} \delta^{\alpha}_{m} \delta^{\beta}_{n} + \Gamma^{\alpha}_{m\lambda} \delta^{\beta}_{n} + \Gamma^{\beta}_{n\lambda} \delta^{\alpha}_{m} \quad (3.27b)$$

and so on.

Clearly the covariant divergence of a vector is the operator:

$$D^{\alpha}_{\alpha m} = \frac{\partial}{\partial x^m} + \Gamma^{\alpha}_{m\alpha}$$

to be applied to F^m and summed over m.

The covariant derivative of the fundamental metric tensor vanishes identically (see (3.20)):

$$\begin{aligned} g^{\alpha\beta}_{;\lambda} = g_{\alpha\beta,\lambda} + \Gamma^{\alpha}_{\lambda\eta} g^{\eta\beta} + \Gamma^{\beta}_{\lambda\eta} g^{\alpha\eta} = 0 \\ g_{\alpha\beta;\lambda} = g_{\alpha\beta,\lambda} - \Gamma^{\eta}_{\alpha\lambda} g_{\eta\beta} - \Gamma^{\eta}_{\beta\lambda} g_{\eta\alpha} = 0 . \end{aligned} \quad (3.28)$$

From this one is able to establish that:

$$\Gamma^{\alpha}_{m\alpha} = \frac{\partial}{\partial x^m} \log \sqrt{-g}$$

where $g = \det(g_{\alpha\beta})$, and hence:

$$F^{\alpha}_{;\alpha} = \left(\frac{\partial}{\partial x^m} + \frac{\partial \log \sqrt{-g}}{\partial x^m}\right) F^m(x) = \frac{1}{\sqrt{-g}} [F^m(x) \sqrt{-g}]_{,m} . \qquad (3.29)$$

In the presence of a gravitational field the charge is:

$$Q = \int \sqrt{(-g)}\, j^{\lambda}(x)\, d\sigma_{\lambda}$$

3.7 THE RIEMANN TENSOR

A space is *flat* when it is possible to carry out a coordinate transformation such that the metric tensor be identical to the Lorentz metric tensor (2.10) everywhere in this space. In it one can make a parallel displacement of any vector throughout and get a constant vector at all points. The ordinary derivative operator is then a vector and two of these operators commute. In a curved space these properties are not valid.

Let us consider the covariant derivative (3.25) of a vector in a curved space, which is a tensor T^{μ}_{α}:

$$T^{\mu}_{\alpha}(x) \equiv F^{\mu}_{;\alpha}(x) = F^{\mu}_{,\alpha}(x) + \Gamma^{\mu}_{\alpha m}(x)\, F^m(x).$$

If we calculate the covariant derivative of this tensor we have (according to (3.26)):

$$\begin{aligned} F^{\mu}_{;\alpha;\lambda} = T^{\mu}_{\alpha;\lambda} &= T^{\mu}_{\alpha,\lambda} + \Gamma^{\mu}_{a\lambda} T^{a}_{\alpha} - \Gamma^{m}_{\alpha\lambda} T^{\mu}_{m} \\ &= F^{\mu}_{,\alpha,\lambda} + (\Gamma^{\mu}_{\alpha\eta})_{,\lambda} F^{\eta} + \Gamma^{\mu}_{\alpha\eta} F^{\eta}_{,\lambda} + \Gamma^{\mu}_{a\lambda} F^{a}_{,\alpha} \\ &\quad - \Gamma^{m}_{\alpha\lambda} F^{\mu}_{,m} + \Gamma^{\mu}_{a\lambda} \Gamma^{a}_{\alpha\eta} F^{\eta} - \Gamma^{m}_{\alpha\lambda} \Gamma^{\mu}_{m\eta} F^{\eta} . \end{aligned}$$

Let us now exchange the indices α and λ and subtract the expression thus obtained from the above one:

$$F^{\mu}_{;\alpha;\lambda} - F^{\mu}_{;\lambda;\alpha} = [(\Gamma^{\mu}_{\alpha\eta})_{,\lambda} - (\Gamma^{\mu}_{\lambda\eta})_{,\alpha} + \Gamma^{\mu}_{a\lambda} \Gamma^{a}_{\alpha\eta} - \Gamma^{\mu}_{a\alpha} \Gamma^{a}_{\lambda\eta}]\, F^{\eta} .$$

In terms of the operators introduced previously, (3.27), we have:

$$(D^{\mu m}_{\alpha\alpha\lambda} - D^{\mu m}_{a\lambda\alpha})\, D^{a}_{\eta m} = R^{\mu}_{\eta\alpha\lambda}$$

where

$$R^{\mu}_{\eta\alpha\lambda} = (\Gamma^{\mu}_{\alpha\eta})_{,\lambda} - (\Gamma^{\mu}_{\lambda\eta})_{,\alpha} + \Gamma^{\mu}_{a\lambda} \Gamma^{a}_{\alpha\eta} - \Gamma^{\mu}_{a\alpha} \Gamma^{a}_{\lambda\eta} \qquad (3.30)$$

is the Riemann curvature tensor.

A flat space by definition is such that:

$$R^{\mu}_{\eta\alpha\lambda}(x) = 0$$

everywhere. Clearly a space with a Lorentz metric has vanishing Γ-symbols and is therefore flat.

We list the following properties of the Riemann tensor:

$$R^{\mu}_{\eta\alpha\lambda} = -R^{\mu}_{\eta\lambda\alpha}$$

$$R_{\mu\alpha\beta\gamma} = g_{\mu\eta}R^{\eta}_{\alpha\beta\gamma} = -R_{\alpha\mu\beta\gamma} = -R_{\mu\alpha\gamma\beta} = R_{\beta\gamma\mu\alpha}$$

$$R_{1023} + R_{2031} + R_{3012} = 0$$

Out of the $4^4 = 256$ components of $R_{\mu\alpha\beta\gamma}$ only 20 are independent, in view of these symmetry properties (as R is antisymmetric in β and γ, these indices, for fixed μ, α, give rise to only 6 independent components instead of 16; similarly for the indices μ, α, for fixed β, γ; hence one would have 36 components; the symmetry with respect to the interchange of $\mu\alpha$ with $\beta\gamma$ reduces these to 21).

3.8 BIANCHI IDENTITIES AND THE RICCI–EINSTEIN TENSOR

In a geodesic coordinate system, the covariant derivative of $R^{\mu}_{\alpha\beta\gamma}$ reduces to:

$$R^{\mu}_{\alpha\beta\gamma;\nu} = (\Gamma^{\mu}_{\alpha\beta})_{,\gamma,\nu} - (\Gamma^{\mu}_{\alpha\gamma})_{,\beta,\nu}.$$

Therefore in this system the following relationship holds:

$$R^{\mu}_{\alpha\beta\gamma;\nu} + R^{\mu}_{\alpha\nu\beta;\gamma} + R^{\mu}_{\alpha\gamma\nu;\beta} = 0. \tag{3.31}$$

These are Bianchi's identities: since the left-hand side is a tensor, the components of which vanish in the geodesic system, the relations hold in any coordinate system.

From the Riemann tensor one can form by contraction a second rank tensor:

$$R_{\mu\nu} = R^{\alpha}_{\mu\alpha\nu}. \tag{3.32}$$

This is the only tensor to be constructed from the Riemann tensor since:

$$R^{\alpha}_{\alpha\mu\nu} = g^{\beta\lambda}R_{\beta\lambda\mu\nu} = g^{\lambda\beta}R_{\lambda\beta\mu\nu} = -g^{\beta\lambda}R_{\beta\lambda\mu\nu} = 0$$

and

$$R^{\alpha}_{\mu\nu\alpha} = -R^{\alpha}_{\mu\alpha\nu} = -R_{\mu\nu}. \tag{3.32a}$$

The explicit form of $R_{\mu\nu}$ is, according to (3.30), (3.32):

$$R_{\mu\nu} = (\Gamma^{\alpha}_{\alpha\mu})_{,\nu} - (\Gamma^{\alpha}_{\mu\nu})_{,\alpha} + \Gamma^{\alpha}_{a\nu}\Gamma^{a}_{\alpha\mu} - \Gamma^{\alpha}_{a\alpha}\Gamma^{a}_{\mu\nu} \qquad (3.33)$$

and it is seen that it is symmetric:

$$R_{\mu\nu} = R_{\nu\mu}.$$

The *scalar curvature* is now defined as the contraction of R^{μ}_{ν}:

$$R = g^{\mu\nu}R_{\mu\nu}. \qquad (3.34)$$

The Ricci–Einstein tensor, G^{μ}_{α}, is one the covariant divergence of which vanishes:

$$G^{\mu}_{\alpha;\mu} = 0. \qquad (3.35)$$

From the Bianchi identities (3.31) we get:

$$R^{\mu\alpha}_{\beta\gamma;\nu} + R^{\mu\alpha}_{\nu\beta;\gamma} + R^{\mu\alpha}_{\gamma\nu;\beta} = 0$$

and the contraction of the indices μ and β gives:

$$R^{\mu\alpha}_{\mu\gamma;\nu} + R^{\mu\alpha}_{\nu\mu;\gamma} + R^{\mu\alpha}_{\gamma\nu;\mu} = 0.$$

Now in view of the definition (3.32) and the symmetry properties (3.32a) one has by contraction of α and γ:

$$R_{;\nu} - R^{\alpha}_{\nu;\alpha} - R^{\mu}_{\nu;\mu} = 0$$

that is:

$$R_{;\nu} = 2R^{\alpha}_{\nu;\alpha}$$

The Einstein–Ricci tensor, which satisfies the equation (3.35) is therefore:

$$G^{\alpha}_{\beta} = R^{\alpha}_{\beta} - \tfrac{1}{2}\delta^{\alpha}_{\beta}R$$

or

$$G_{\alpha\beta} = R_{\alpha\beta} - \tfrac{1}{2}g_{\alpha\beta}R. \qquad (3.36)$$

3.9 EINSTEIN'S GRAVITATIONAL FIELD EQUATIONS

It is seen, in view of the definitions (3.36), (3.34), (3.33) and the expression (3.21), that $G_{\alpha\beta}$ contains, besides non-linear combinations of $g_{\mu\nu}$ and $g_{\mu\nu,\lambda}$ second derivatives of the metric tensor (or gravitational potential field) $g_{\mu\nu}(x)$ (linearly). If the energy momentum tensor of matter, $T_{\mu\nu}$, must obey the covariant equation which generalises equation (2.41a) into a Riemannian space:

$$T^{\mu}_{\nu;\mu} = 0$$

then, in view of the relation (3.35) it is plausible to postulate that the gravitational field equations are of the form:

$$G^{\alpha}_{\beta} = KT^{\alpha}_{\beta} \tag{3.36a}$$

where K is a coupling constant. This was the postulate proposed by Einstein in 1915 after several years of attempts at discovering the relativistic equations which may be regarded as a generalisation of Poisson's equation (3.1).

The reader is referred to the literature[(7)] if he is interested in the mathematical structure of Einstein's equations and their consequences. In the particular case of a time-independent and weak gravitational field (i.e. differing very little from the Lorentz metric tensor) the identification with Poisson's equation is achieved if one sets:

$$K = \frac{8\pi G}{c^2}.$$

The energy–momentum tensor $T_{\mu\nu}$ contains the contribution of all matter and fields except the gravitational field. The equations ot these fields, however, take into account the gravitational field, in the differentiation operators. Thus, the equations of a gravitational field produced by an electromagnetic radiation field (in the absence of charges) are:

$$G_{\mu\nu} = KT_{\mu\nu} \tag{3.37}$$

where

$$T_{\mu\nu} = F_{\mu m}F^{m}_{\nu} + \tfrac{1}{4}g_{\mu\nu}F_{mn}F^{mn}$$

is the energy–momentum tensor of the radiation field determined by the equations:

$$(\sqrt{(-g)}\,F^{\mu\nu})_{,\nu} = 0$$

$$F_{\mu\nu,\lambda} + F_{\lambda\mu,\nu} + F_{\nu\lambda,\mu} = 0 \qquad F_{\mu\nu} = A_{\nu,\mu} - A_{\mu,\nu}.$$

In this case, since $T_{\mu\nu}$ is traceless

$$T \equiv T^{\mu}_{\mu} = 0.$$

Einstein's equations, which have the equivalent form:

$$R_{\mu\nu} = K(T_{\mu\nu} - \tfrac{1}{2}g_{\mu\nu}T)$$

reduce to

$$R_{\mu\nu} = KT_{\mu\nu}$$

3.10 THE GRAVITATIONAL FIELD ENERGY-MOMENTUM PSEUDO-TENSOR. EINSTEIN'S VARIATIONAL PRINCIPLE

The extension of the equation (2.41a) to a Riemannian space is:

$$T^{\mu\nu}_{;\nu} = 0$$

and this is imposed by Einstein's equations. We have, according to (3.26):

$$T^{\mu\nu}_{,\nu} + \Gamma^{\mu}_{\lambda\eta} T^{\lambda\eta} + \Gamma^{\eta}_{\lambda\eta} T^{\mu\lambda} = 0$$

or

$$T^{\nu}_{\alpha,\nu} + \Gamma^{\eta}_{\lambda\eta} T^{\lambda}_{\alpha} - \Gamma^{\lambda}_{\alpha\eta} T^{\eta}_{\lambda} = 0. \tag{3.38}$$

Therefore we cannot define a conserved quantity of the form (2.41b). The meaning of this relationship is the following: the tensor $T_{\mu\nu}$, source of the gravitational field, cannot be conserved alone; the gravitational field interacts with itself, since it gives rise to an additional energy which, in turn, contributes to this field. It is thus not unexpected that only a combination of the original $T_{\mu\nu}$ and of gravitational field quantities can be conserved.

The question then arises whether it is possible to separate this conserved quantity into two parts, one associated to the source, the other to the gravitational field. We are going to show, following mainly Adler *et al.*[(7)], that it is possible to transform the equation (3.38) into one of the following type:

$$(\sqrt{(-g)}\, T^{\nu}_{\alpha} + \sqrt{(-g)}\, t^{\nu}_{\alpha})_{,\nu} = 0 \tag{3.39}$$

which is of the usual form (2.41) and which allows us to construct a conserved object:

$$P_{\alpha} = \int d\sigma_{\nu} \sqrt{(-g)}\, (T^{\nu}_{\alpha} + t^{\nu}_{\alpha}). \tag{3.40}$$

This object is however, *not* a vector since it turns out that the quantity t^{ν}_{α} is *not* a tensor. Therefore the meaning attached to such an object, which depends on the coordinate system, is not quite clear.

From the expression (3.21) for the Christoffel symbols, one gets:

$$\Gamma^{\eta}_{\lambda\eta} = \frac{1}{2} g^{\nu\beta} \frac{\partial g_{\nu\beta}}{\partial x^{\lambda}}$$

since:

$$g^{\nu\beta} \left(\frac{\partial g_{\lambda\beta}}{\partial x^{\nu}} - \frac{\partial g_{\lambda\nu}}{\partial x^{\beta}} \right) = g^{\nu\beta} \frac{\partial g_{\lambda\beta}}{\partial x^{\nu}} - g^{\beta\nu} \frac{\partial g_{\lambda\beta}}{\partial x^{\nu}} = 0.$$

Therefore, according to (3.19):

$$\Gamma^{\eta}_{\lambda\eta} = \frac{1}{2g}\frac{\partial g}{\partial x^{\lambda}} = (\log\sqrt{-g})_{,\lambda} = \frac{(\sqrt{-g})_{,\lambda}}{\sqrt{-g}}. \tag{3.41}$$

On the other hand, as the tensor $T^{\mu\nu}$ is symmetric, we may write:

$$\Gamma^{\lambda}_{\alpha\eta}T^{\eta}_{\lambda} = \tfrac{1}{2}(\Gamma_{\lambda,\alpha\eta} + \Gamma_{\eta,\alpha\lambda})\,T^{\lambda\eta}$$

so, in view of equation (3.22):

$$\Gamma^{\lambda}_{\alpha\eta}T^{\eta}_{\lambda} = \frac{1}{2}\frac{\partial g_{\lambda\eta}}{\partial x^{\alpha}}\,T^{\lambda\eta}.$$

Thus the equation (3.38) becomes:

$$T^{\nu}_{\alpha,\nu} + \frac{(\sqrt{-g})_{,\lambda}}{\sqrt{-g}}\,T^{\lambda}_{\alpha} - \frac{1}{2}\,g_{\lambda\eta,\alpha}T^{\lambda\eta} = 0$$

or:

$$\frac{1}{\sqrt{-g}}\,(T^{\nu}_{\alpha}\sqrt{-g})_{,\nu} - \frac{1}{2}\,g_{\lambda\eta,\alpha}T^{\lambda\eta} = 0.$$

Einstein's equations allow us to write:

$$(T^{\nu}_{\alpha}\sqrt{-g})_{,\nu} - \frac{1}{2}\,g_{\lambda\eta,\alpha}\sqrt{(-g)}\,\frac{1}{K}\left(R^{\lambda\eta} - \frac{1}{2}\,g^{\lambda\eta}R\right) = 0.$$

It is seen that the problem of establishing equation (3.39) reduces to finding a quantity t^{ν}_{α} such that:

$$(\sqrt{(-g)}\,t^{\nu}_{\alpha})_{,\nu} = -\frac{1}{2}\,g_{\lambda\eta,\alpha}\sqrt{(-g)}\,\frac{1}{K}\,G^{\lambda\eta} \tag{3.42}$$

Let us then consider the Einstein's gravitational action S_g:

$$S_g = \int_{\varrho} R\sqrt{(-g)}\,d^4x \qquad R = g^{\mu\nu}R_{\lambda\nu} \tag{3.43}$$

where the integration is taken over a certain domain ϱ of four-dimensional space. R, the scalar curvature, is invariant; $\sqrt{(-g)}\,d^4x$ is another invariant, hence S_g is a scalar functional.

The variation of S_g with respect to a variation of the field $g_{\mu\nu}$ such that

$$\delta g_{\mu\nu} = \delta g_{\mu\nu,\lambda} = 0 \quad \text{on the boundary of } \varrho$$

is:

$$\delta S_g = \int [\sqrt{(-g)}\,g^{\mu\nu}\,\delta R_{\mu\nu} + g^{\mu\nu}R_{\mu\nu}\delta\,(\sqrt{(-g)}) + R_{\mu\nu}\sqrt{(-g)}\,\delta g^{\mu\nu}]\,d^4x.$$

In a geodesic coordinate system, according to (3.33), (3.23a):

$$\delta R_{\mu\nu} = \delta\,(\Gamma^{\alpha}_{\alpha\mu})_{,\nu} - \delta(\Gamma^{\alpha}_{\mu\nu})_{,\alpha}.$$

In this system, the ordinary derivative coincides with the covariant derivative, hence:

$$\delta R_{\mu\nu} = \delta(\Gamma^{\alpha}_{\alpha\mu})_{;\nu} - \delta(\Gamma^{\alpha}_{\mu\nu})_{;\alpha}.$$

Since both sides of this equation are tensors (the reader will show that although $\Gamma^{\lambda}_{\alpha\beta}$ is not a tensor, $\delta\Gamma^{\lambda}_{\alpha\beta}$ *is a tensor*) the equation is generally valid.

On the other hand, the relations (3.17), (3.18) lead us to write:

$$\delta(\sqrt{-g}) = -\tfrac{1}{2}(\sqrt{-g})\, g_{\mu\nu}\, \delta g^{\mu\nu}$$

Therefore:

$$\delta S_g = \int_{\varrho} \sqrt{(-g)}\, [\delta(\Gamma^{\alpha}_{\alpha\mu})_{;\nu} - \delta(\Gamma^{\alpha}_{\mu\nu})_{;\alpha}]\, g^{\mu\nu}\, d^4x + \int_{\varrho} G_{\mu\nu} \sqrt{(-g)}\, \delta g^{\mu\nu}\, d^4x.$$

The first integral can be transformed into an integral over the boundary of ϱ. Indeed, let us set:

$$g^{\mu\nu}\, [\delta(\Gamma^{\alpha}_{\alpha\mu})_{;\nu} - \delta(\Gamma^{\alpha}_{\mu\nu})_{;\alpha}] = (g^{\mu\nu}\delta\Gamma^{\alpha}_{\alpha\mu})_{;\nu} - (g^{\mu\nu}\delta\Gamma^{\alpha}_{\mu\nu})_{;\alpha}$$

since $g^{\mu\nu}_{;\alpha} = 0$. Now, as $\delta\Gamma^{\lambda}_{\alpha\beta}$ is a tensor we can write:

$$(g^{\mu\nu}\delta\Gamma^{\alpha}_{\alpha\mu})_{;\nu} - (g^{\mu\nu}\delta\Gamma^{\alpha}_{\mu\nu})_{;\alpha} = A^{\nu}_{;\nu} - B^{\alpha}_{;\alpha}$$

where A^{ν} and B^{ν} are two vectors. Therefore, according to the divergence formula (3.29):

$$\int_{\varrho} \sqrt{(-g)}\, [\delta(\Gamma^{\alpha}_{\alpha\mu})_{;\nu} - \delta(\Gamma^{\alpha}_{\mu\nu})_{;\alpha}]\, g^{\mu\nu}\, \mathrm{d}^4x = \int_{\text{boundary}} \sqrt{(-g)}\, [A^{\nu} - B^{\nu}]\, \mathrm{d}\sigma_{\nu}.$$

A^{ν} and B^{ν}, however, vanish on the boundary of ϱ because $\delta g^{\mu\nu}$ and $\delta\Gamma^{\lambda}_{\alpha\beta}$ vanish there. We are thus left with:

$$\delta S_g = \int_{\varrho} G_{\mu\nu} \sqrt{(-g)}\, \delta g^{\mu\nu}\, d^4x$$

whence:

$$\frac{\delta S_g}{\delta g^{\mu\nu}} = \sqrt{(-g)}\, G_{\mu\nu}. \tag{3.44}$$

This result shows that if one can construct a Lagrangian density $L_m\sqrt{-g}$ depending upon the gravitational field $g_{\mu\nu}$, the matter and other fields, and such that the variation of the action:

$$S_m = \int_\varrho L_m \sqrt{(-g)}\, d^4x \tag{3.45}$$

be equal to

$$\delta S_m = -K \int_\varrho T_{\mu\nu} \sqrt{(-g)}\, \delta g^{\mu\nu}\, d^4x$$

then *Einstein's equations* (3.36a) *are deducible from a variational principle:*

$$\delta S = 0$$

where

$$S = S_g + S_m$$

according to (3.43) and (3.45) and $\delta g^{\mu\nu} = 0$, $\delta g^{\mu\nu}_{,\lambda} = 0$ over the boundary of ϱ.

Let us now go back to the construction of an object t^ν_α satisfying equation (3.39). We first *split the scalar density* $R\sqrt{-g}$, equ. (3.34), *into a sum of terms which contain first derivatives of* $g_{\mu\nu}$ *at most and another term which is the sum of divergencies.* The idea is, by transforming away these divergences, to reduce $R\sqrt{-g}$ to another form $\mathscr{L}$ which contains at most first derivatives in $g_{\mu\nu}$. This is so because only then will the Lagrange equations yield field equations containing second derivatives of $g_{\mu\nu}(x)$ at most, as postulated by Einstein. In view of the identity:

$$\begin{aligned}\sqrt{(-g)}\, g^{\mu\nu} [(\Gamma^\alpha_{\alpha\mu})_{,\nu} - (\Gamma^\alpha_{\mu\nu})_{,\alpha}] &= (\sqrt{(-g)}\, g^{\mu\nu}\Gamma^\alpha_{\alpha\mu})_{,\nu} - (\sqrt{(-g)}\, g^{\mu\nu}\Gamma^\alpha_{\mu\nu})_{,\alpha} \\ &\quad + (\sqrt{(-g)}\, g^{\mu\nu})_{,\alpha}\Gamma^\alpha_{\mu\nu} - (\sqrt{(-g)}\, g^{\mu\nu})_{,\nu}\Gamma^\alpha_{\alpha\mu}\end{aligned}$$

one may write, in view of (3.33) and (3.34):

$$R\sqrt{(-g)} = (\sqrt{(-g)}\, g^{\mu\nu}\Gamma^\alpha_{\alpha\mu})_{,\nu} - (\sqrt{(-g)}\, g^{\mu\nu}\Gamma^\alpha_{\alpha\nu})_{,\alpha} + \mathscr{L}$$

where

$$\begin{aligned}\mathscr{L} = \sqrt{(-g)}\, g^{\mu\nu} [\Gamma^\alpha_{a\nu}\Gamma^a_{\alpha\mu} - \Gamma^\alpha_{a\alpha}\Gamma^a_{\mu\nu}] + (\sqrt{(-g)}\, g^{\mu\nu})_{,\alpha}\Gamma^\alpha_{\mu\nu} \\ - (\sqrt{(-g)}\, g^{\mu\nu})_{,\nu}\Gamma^\alpha_{\alpha\mu}\end{aligned}$$

can be transformed into (see (3.28 and (3.41)):

$$\mathscr{L} = \sqrt{(-g)}\, g^{\mu\nu} [\Gamma^\alpha_{\mu\nu}\Gamma^m_{m\alpha} - \Gamma^m_{\alpha\mu}\Gamma^\alpha_{m\nu}].$$

Therefore the action S_g, (3.43), transforms into:

$$S_g = \int_\varrho \mathscr{L}\, \mathrm{d}^4x + \int_{\text{bound}} \sqrt{(-g)}\, g^{\mu\nu}\Gamma^\alpha_{\alpha\mu}\, d\sigma_\nu - \int_{\text{bound}} \sqrt{(-g)}\, g^{\mu\nu}\Gamma^\alpha_{\mu\nu}\, d\sigma_\alpha.$$

Thus, for variations such that $\delta g_{\mu\nu}$ and $\delta g_{\mu\nu,\lambda}$ vanish at the boundary, the variational derivative of S_g will be equal to that of the first term above:

$$\left.\begin{aligned} E &= \int_\varrho \mathscr{L}\, d^4x \\ \frac{\delta S_g}{\delta g_{\mu\nu}} &= \frac{\delta E}{\delta g_{\mu\nu}}. \end{aligned}\right\} \tag{3.46}$$

The important point here is that $\mathscr{L}$ is not a scalar density.

Now:

$$\begin{aligned} \delta E &= \int_\varrho \left[\frac{\partial \mathscr{L}}{\partial g^{\mu\nu}}\, \delta g^{\mu\nu} + \frac{\partial \mathscr{L}}{\partial g^{\mu\nu}_{,\lambda}}\, \partial g^{\mu\nu}_{,\lambda}\right] d^4x \\ &= \int_\varrho \left[\frac{\partial \mathscr{L}}{\partial g^{\mu\nu}} - \left(\frac{\partial \mathscr{L}}{\partial g^{\mu\nu}_{,\lambda}}\right)_{,\lambda}\right] \delta g^{\mu\nu}\, d^4x + \int_{\text{bound}} \frac{\partial \mathscr{L}}{\partial g^{\mu\nu}_{,\lambda}}\, \delta g^{\mu\nu}\, d\sigma_\lambda \end{aligned}$$

and the last integral vanishes if $\delta g^{\mu\nu} = 0$ at the boundary. Therefore, in view of (3.44) and (3.46):

$$\sqrt{(-g)}\, G_{\mu\nu} = \frac{\partial \mathscr{L}}{\partial g^{\mu\nu}} - \left(\frac{\partial \mathscr{L}}{\partial g^{\mu\nu}_{,\lambda}}\right)_{,\lambda}.$$

Let us multiply both sides of this equation by $g^{\mu\nu}_{,\alpha}$, and remark that:

$$\mathscr{L}_{,\alpha} = \frac{\partial \mathscr{L}}{\partial g^{mn}}\, g^{mn}_{,\alpha} + \frac{\partial \mathscr{L}}{\partial g^{mn}_{,\eta}}\, g^{mn}_{,\eta,\alpha}$$

to get

$$g^{\mu\nu}_{,\alpha} \sqrt{(-g)}\, G_{\mu\nu} = \mathscr{L}_{,\alpha} - \left(\frac{\partial \mathscr{L}}{\partial g^{mn}_{,\lambda}}\, g^{mn}_{,\alpha}\right)_{,\lambda} = \left(\mathscr{L}\delta^\lambda_\alpha - \frac{\partial \mathscr{L}}{\partial g^{mn}_{,\lambda}}\, g^{mn}_{,\alpha}\right)_{,\lambda}. \tag{3.47}$$

Clearly, from the definition:

$$g^{\mu\nu} g_{\mu\eta} = \delta^\nu_\eta$$

one has

$$g^{\mu\nu}_{,\alpha} g_{\mu\eta} + g^{\mu\nu} g_{\mu\eta,\alpha} = 0$$

hence

$$\sqrt{(-g)}\, g^{\mu\nu}_{,\alpha} G_{\mu\nu} = \sqrt{(-g)}\, g^{\mu\nu}_{,\alpha} g_{\mu m} g_{\nu n} G^{mn} = -\sqrt{(-g)}\, g_{\mu m,\alpha} G^{\mu m}. \tag{3.47a}$$

Therefore, if this equation is compared with equations (3.42), (3.47) then one may define the quantity t^ν_α by means of the relation:

$$\sqrt{(-g)}\, t^\nu_\alpha = \frac{1}{2K}\left(\mathscr{L}\delta^\nu_\alpha - \frac{\partial \mathscr{L}}{\partial g^{mn}_{,\nu}}\, g^{mn}_{,\alpha}\right)$$

and this quantity—the so-called *energy–momentum pseudo-tensor of the gravitational field*—satisfies the conservation law (3.39).

Since $\mathscr{L}$ is not a scalar density, it follows that t_α^ν is not a tensor. One thus understands that although it is possible to construct the object P_α given in (3.40), which is conserved, this object is not generally a four-vector and depends on the coordinate system.

Other quantities have been constructed by different authors (Landau–Lifshitz, Möller, etc.) and the object t_α^ν is thus not uniquely defined.

Such difficulties still remain in an alternative field theory of gravitation[8] the basic equations of which are of the form:

$$\Box \phi_{\mu\nu} = K(T_{\mu\nu} - \tfrac{1}{2}g_{\mu\nu}T_\alpha^\alpha)$$

the symmetric tensor $\phi_{\mu\nu}$ describing this field in a flat space. As shown by Thirring one is led in such a theory to "renormalize" the metric and introduce a metric $g_{\mu\nu}(x)$ which depends on the field $\phi_{\mu\nu}(x)$.

The fact that the gravitational field has a universal interaction not only with all other fields but also with itself, leads to the non-linear effects which are essentially responsible for the difficulty in the construction of an energy–momentum tensor associated to the gravitational field. On the other hand, the fact that it is always possible, in Einstein's theory, to choose a geodesic system in an arbitrary point of space–time, means that locally the gravitational field is transformed away and that, therefore, at this point the energy and momentum of this field can be made to vanish. Therefore, the energy–momentum object cannot be a tensor and has to depend on the coordinate system.

References to Part One

1. HERMANN WEYL, *Symmetry*, Princeton University Press (1952). This book was written before it was discovered (1957) that the laws of nature do not all have bilateral symmetry. See, for instance, C. N. YANG, *Elementary Particles*, Princeton University Press (1961).
2. R. M. F. HOUTAPPEL, H. VAN DAM, and E. P. WIGNER, "The conceptual basis and use of the geometric invariance principles", *Rev. Mod. Phys.37*, 595, (1965). See also, E. P. WIGNER, "Symmetry and conservation laws", *Proc. Natl. Acad. Sci.* (U.S.), **51**, 956 (1964). See also B.VITALE and G.MAIELLA, *A Note on dynamical symmetries of classical systems*, Preprint Univ. di Napoli (1966); B.Vitale *et al.*, *Conserved quantities and symmetry groups for the Kepler problem*, ibid. (1966).
3. See, for instance, A.N.KOLMOGOROV and S.V.FOMIN, *Functional Analysis*, Vol.1, 2, Graylock Press, Rochester (1957). The reader will also be interested in completing his knowledge of mathematical tools through the following publications:
   L. SCHWARTZ, *Methodes Mathématiques pour les Sciences Physiques*, Hermann, Paris (1965); *Théorie des Distributions*, Hermann, Paris **I**, II (1957–59).
   I. M. GUELFAND and G.E.CHILOV, *Les Distributions*, I–V, Dunod, Paris (1962).
   L. GARDING and J.LIONS, "Functional analysis", *Nuovo Cimento Suppl.* **14**, 9 (1959).
   E. P. WIGNER, *Group Theory and its Applications to Quantum Mechanics*, Academic Press, New York (1959).
   H.CARTAN, *Théorie Elémentaire des Fonctions Analytiques d'Une ou Plusieurs Variables Complexes*, Hermann, Paris (1961).
   L.B. VAN DER WAERDEN, *Modern Algebra*, F.Ungar Publ. Co., New York (1964).
4. C.MÖLLER, *Theory of Relativity*, Clarendon Press, Oxford (1952).
5. For instance, J.LEITE-LOPES, *Fondements de la Physique Atomique*, Hermann, Paris (1967).
6. E.P.WIGNER, "Unitary representations of the inhomogeneous Lorentz group", *Ann. Math.* **40**, 149 (1939).
   M.A.NAIMARK, *Les Représentations Linéaires du Groupe de Lorentz*, Dunod, Paris (1962).
   I. M. GUELFAND, R.A.MINLOS and Z. YA SHAPIRO, *Representations of the Rotation and Lorentz groups and their Applications*, Pergamon Press, Oxford (1963).
   J.WERLE, *Relativistic Theory of Reactions*, North-Holland, Amsterdam (1966).
   F. J. DYSON (Ed.), *Symmetry groups in Nuclear and Particle Physics*, Benjamin, New York (1966).
7. R.ADLER, M.BAZIN, M.SCHIFFER, *Introduction to General Relativity*, McGraw-Hill, New York (1965). (And the bibliographical references this textbook gives.)
   J. WEBER, *General Relativity and Gravitational Waves*, Interscience Publ., New York (1961).

Louis Witten ed., *Gravitation: An Introduction to Current Research*, John Wiley, New York (1962).

R. H. Dicke, *The Theoretical Significance of Experimental Relativity*, Gordon and Breach, New York (1964).

L. Landau and E. M. Lifshitz, *Théorie des Champs*, Editions de la Paix, Moscou.

V. Fock, *The Theory of Space, Time and Gravitation*, Pergamon Press, New York (1959).

P. G. Bergmann, The general theory of relativity, in *Handbuch der Physik*, vol. 4, Berlin–Göttingen–Heidelberg (1962).

A. Lichnerowicz, *Théories Relativistes de la Gravitation et de l'Electromagnétisme*, Masson ed., Paris (1955).

8. W. E. Thirring, "An alternative approach to the theory of gravitation", *Ann. Phys.* **16**, 96 (1961); also the review by T. W. Kibble, "The quantum theory of gravitation" in *High Energy Physics and Elementary Particles*, International Atomic Energy Agency, Vienna (1965).

Part Two

INVERSION OPERATIONS IN QUANTUM FIELD THEORY

CHAPTER 1

Review of The Foundations of Quantum Field Theory

1.1 LORENTZ TRANSFORMATION OF FIELD OPERATORS

In relativistic quantum theory, the wave fields are postulated to be operators which act on a Hilbert space. These operators are determined by the field equations and the commutation rules (to within a unitary transformation). These operators also depend on discrete variables—the spinor and tensor indices—which are determined by the requirement that they be elements of a finite-dimensional representation space of the inhomogeneous proper Lorentz group (from which we shall also exclude the time inversions in this chapter).

The state vectors $|\Psi\rangle$ (or kets) are elements of the Hilbert space. The relativistic invariance of the theory requires that the transformed

$$|\Psi'\rangle = \mathrm{U(L)}\,|\Psi\rangle \tag{1}$$

corresponding to an inhomogenous proper Lorentz transformation L:

$$x^{\mu'} = l^{\mu}_{\nu}x^{\nu} + a^{\mu}; \quad g_{\mu\nu}l^{\mu}_{\lambda}l^{\nu}_{\tau} = g_{\lambda\tau}; \quad l^{0}_{0} \geqq 1 \tag{2}$$

be also a possible state of the system. The operators U form an infinite-dimensional representation of this (Poincaré) group and are unitary:

$$\mathrm{U(L)}^{+}\,\mathrm{U(L)} = \mathrm{I} = \mathrm{U(L)}\,\mathrm{U(L)}^{+}$$

so that:

$$\langle\Psi'|\Phi'\rangle = \langle\Psi|\Phi\rangle.$$

Let $|\Psi\rangle$ be the state vector and O(x) be operators associated to a physical system by an observer in a frame of reference. The physicist of another Lorentz frame may either: (*a*) ascribe to the system the same state vector $|\Psi\rangle$ and new operators O′(x), or (*b*) decribe the system by means of a new state vector $|\Psi'\rangle$ and unchanged operators O(x). The first method is the Heisenberg-type of Lorentz transformation in the Hilbert space, the second is the Schrödinger type.

Both methods must be equivalent in the sense that both must give the same expectation values for the physical quantities.

Thus:

$$\langle \Psi' | O'(x) | \Psi' \rangle_H = \langle \Psi' | O'(x) | \Psi' \rangle_S$$

or:

$$\langle \Psi | O'(x) | \Psi \rangle = \langle \Psi' | O(x) | \Psi' \rangle \tag{3}$$

hence:

$$O'(x) = U^+(L)\, O(x)\, U(L). \tag{4}$$

The form of $O'(x)$, on the other hand, is obtained by the requirement that the field equations be invariant under the proper Poincaré group. The study of the finite-dimensional representations (irreducible) of this group yields the result that the field variables can only be scalars, spinors, four-vectors, and tensors and spinors of higher rank. Thus, a scalar field $\varphi(x)$ is such that:

$$\varphi'(x') \equiv U^+(L)\, \varphi(x')\, U(L) = \varphi(x); \tag{5}$$

a vector field operator $A^\mu(x)$ satisfies:

$$A^{\mu'}(x') \equiv U^+(L)\, A^\mu(x')\, U(L) = l^\mu_\nu A^\nu(x) \tag{6}$$

and for a Dirac spinor one has:

$$\psi'(x') \equiv U^+(L)\, \psi(x')\, U(L) = D\psi(x). \tag{7}$$

Where D is such that:

$$D\gamma^\mu D^{-1} = l^\mu_k \gamma^k; \quad l^\mu_k = g_{k\lambda} l^\lambda_\nu g^{\nu\mu}, \tag{8}$$

and:

$$\gamma^\mu\gamma^\nu + \gamma^\nu\gamma^\mu = 2g^{\mu\nu}, \quad g^{00} = -g^{11} = -g^{22} = -g^{33} = 1;$$

$$g^{\mu\nu} = 0, \quad \mu \neq \nu \tag{9}$$

and for a free spinor field:

$$\left(i\gamma^\mu \frac{\partial}{\partial x^\mu} - m \right) \psi(x) = 0. \tag{10}$$

We remark that while the transformations U(L) which constitute an infinite-dimensional representation of the Poincaré group can be taken as unitary, the transformations such as L, D, which transform the (finite-dimensional) 4-vector and spinor space into themselves respectively, can*not* be unitary.

For an infinitesimal proper Lorentz transformation:

$$l^{\mu}_{\nu} = \delta^{\mu}_{\nu} + \varepsilon^{\mu}_{\nu}, \tag{11}$$

one gets:

$$\mathrm{D}(\varepsilon) = \mathrm{I} - \frac{i}{2}\,\varepsilon_{\mu\nu}D^{\mu\nu} \tag{12}$$

$$D^{\mu\nu} = \frac{i}{4}\,(\gamma^{\mu}\gamma^{\nu} - \gamma^{\nu}\gamma^{\mu}). \tag{13}$$

Thus, because:

$$(\gamma^{\mu})^{+} = \gamma^{0}\gamma^{\mu}\gamma^{0} \tag{14}$$

one has:

$$(D^{\mu\nu})^{+} = \gamma^{0}D^{\mu\nu}\gamma^{0} \tag{15}$$

and

$$\mathrm{D}(\varepsilon)^{+} = \gamma^{0}\mathrm{D}^{-1}\gamma^{0}.$$

A finite proper transformation gives:

$$\mathrm{D} = e^{\frac{1}{8}\varepsilon_{\mu\nu}(\gamma^{\mu}\gamma^{\nu} - \gamma^{\nu}\gamma^{\mu})}. \tag{16}$$

For space rotations one has:

$$\mathrm{D}_{\mathrm{R}}^{+} = \mathrm{D}_{\mathrm{R}}^{-1}$$

because:

$$\gamma^{0}\gamma^{i}\gamma^{k}\gamma^{0} = \gamma^{i}\gamma^{k} \quad i, k = 1, 2, 3.$$

What is the form of U(L) corresponding to an infinitesimal Lorentz transformation? Let L be the lagrangian density constructed with the field operators O(x) and their first space-time derivatives in an invariant fashion under the proper Poincaré group and such that the variation of the action:

$$\mathrm{I} = \int L\left[\mathrm{O}(x), \frac{\partial \mathrm{O}(x)}{\partial x^{\mu}}\right] d^{4}x$$

give rise to the field equations.

L is known from classical field theory. However, when the fields are operators, one must define the order in which they are taken in products, since they in general do not commute.

L will be taken as the expression in classical theory, the operators being ordered as *normal products*. This will be defined later and adopted for all observables such as current density $j^{\mu}_{(x)}$, angular momentum tensor $M^{\mu\nu}$, energy–momentum tensor $T^{\mu\nu}$, energy–momentum vector P^{μ}:

$$P^{\mu} = \int d^3x\, T^{0\mu} \quad (\equiv \int d\sigma_{\alpha}\, T^{\alpha\mu}) \tag{17}$$

$$T^{\mu\nu} = g^{\alpha\nu} \frac{\partial L}{\partial\left(\dfrac{\partial O_i(x)}{\partial x^{\mu}}\right)} \frac{\partial O_i(x)}{\partial x^{\alpha}} - L g^{\mu\nu} \tag{18}$$

$$M^{\mu\nu} = \int d^3x\, M^{0;\mu\nu} \quad (\equiv \int d\sigma_{\alpha} M^{\alpha;\mu\nu}) \tag{19}$$

(integration over space-like surface $\int d\sigma_{\alpha}$ shows the covariance of P^{μ} and $M^{\mu\nu}$)

$$M^{\lambda;\mu\nu} = g^{\mu\alpha} g^{\nu\beta} M^{\lambda}_{\alpha\beta} \tag{20}$$

$$M^{\lambda}_{\alpha\beta} = T^{\lambda}_{\alpha} x_{\beta} - T^{\lambda}_{\beta} x_{\alpha} - \frac{\partial L}{\partial\left(\dfrac{\partial O_i(x)}{\partial x^{\lambda}}\right)} D_{ij;\alpha\beta} O_j(x). \tag{21}$$

Here, the $D_{ij;\alpha\beta}$ are the infinitesimal operators of the transformation of the field variables in spinor or tensor space (12). Thus, for a scalar field

$$D_{ij;\alpha\beta} = 0 \tag{22}$$

for a vector field:

$$D_{ij;\alpha\beta} = \delta^j_{\beta} g_{i\alpha} - \delta^j_{\alpha} g_{i\beta} \quad i, j, \alpha, \beta = 0, 1, 2, 3; \tag{23}$$

for a spinor field:

$$D_{ij;\alpha\beta} = \tfrac{1}{4}(\gamma_{\alpha}\gamma_{\beta} - \gamma_{\beta}\gamma_{\alpha})_{ij}. \tag{24}$$

Now, then, an infinitesimal unitary transformation $U(a, \varepsilon)$ in Hilbert space corresponding to an infinitesimal inhomogenous Lorentz transformation:

$$x^{\mu'} = (\delta^{\mu}_{\nu} + \varepsilon^{\mu}_{\nu})\, x^{\nu} + a^{\mu},$$

is of the form:

$$U(a, \varepsilon) = I - i a_{\mu} P^{\mu} - \frac{i}{2} \varepsilon_{\mu\nu} M^{\mu\nu}. \tag{25}$$

U is unitary, the energy–momentum vector and the angular momentum tensor are hermitian. The latter are seen to be the infinitesimal operators which determine the infinite-dimensional representations (unitary) of the inhomogenous Lorentz group. For finite transformations:

$$U(L) = \exp\left(-ia_\mu P^\mu - \frac{i}{2}\,\varepsilon_{\mu\nu}M^{\mu\nu}\right). \tag{26}$$

1.2 CONDITIONS IMPOSED BY U ON THE FIELD OPERATORS

The existence of a unitary transformation U(L) which transforms O into O′:

$$O'(x) = U^+(L)\,O(x)\,U(L) \tag{4}$$

imposes certain conditions on the field variables $O(x)$. They must satisfy given commutation rules with P^μ and $M^{\mu\nu}$.

Indeed, let:

$$x^{\mu'} = x^\mu + f^\mu_\nu \omega^\nu \tag{27}$$

be an infinitesimal linear transformations on x, with infinitesimal parameters ω^ν. In the case of a proper Lorentz infinitesimal transformation, the index ν is a pair of indices $\alpha\beta$ and:

$$\omega^\nu \to \varepsilon^{\alpha\beta}$$

$$f^\mu_\nu \to f^\mu_{\alpha\beta} = \delta^\mu_\alpha g_{\beta\nu}x^\nu - \delta^\mu_\beta g_{\alpha\nu}x^\nu, \quad \alpha \leqq \beta. \tag{28}$$

In the case of a translation:

$$f^\mu_\nu = \delta^\mu_\nu, \quad \omega^\nu = a^\nu. \tag{29}$$

Transformation (27) induces a transformation of the field operators, in their arguments x and their form, $O(x) \to O'(x')$ and we shall write:

$$O'_i(x') = O_i(x) + \Omega_{ij}(x)\,\omega^j. \tag{30}$$

The variation of the operator is:

$$\delta O_i(x) \equiv O'_i(x') - O_i(x) = \Omega_{ij}(x)\,\omega^j \tag{31}$$

while the variation in form only is:

$$\bar{\delta} O_i(x) \equiv O'_i(x) - O_i(x) = O'_i(x') - O_i(x) - (O'_i(x') - O'_i(x))$$

$$= \Omega_{ij}(x)\,\omega^j - \frac{\partial O'_i}{\partial x^k}\,\delta x^k = \left(\Omega_{ij}(x) - \frac{\partial O_i}{\partial x^k} f^k_j\right)\omega^j. \tag{32}$$

On the other hand, (27) induces an infinitesimal unitary transformation $U(\omega)$ in Hilbert space which transforms the operators according to (4).

If we call $\delta U(\omega)$ the infinitesimal part of $U(\omega)$:

$$U(\omega) = I + \delta U(\omega) \tag{33}$$

then the unitarity of $U(\omega)$ gives:

$$(\delta U(\omega))^+ = -\delta U(\omega)$$

and (4) will be:

$$\begin{aligned} O_i'(x) &= U^+(\omega)\, O_i(x)\, U(\omega) = (I - \delta U(\omega))\, O_i(x)\, (I + \delta U(\omega)) \\ &= O_i(x) + [O_i(x), \delta U(\omega)] \end{aligned} \tag{34}$$

where

$$[A, B] = AB - BA.$$

Thus

$$O_i'(x) - O_i(x) \equiv \bar{\delta} O_i(x) = [O_i(x), \delta U(\omega)]$$

$\delta U(\omega)$ is linear in the parameters ω, so we write:

$$\delta U(\omega) = i U_\nu \omega^\nu$$

to get:

$$\bar{\delta} O_i(x) = i\, [O_i(x), U_\nu]\, \omega^\nu. \tag{35}$$

Compare (35) with (32), you obtain:

$$\boxed{i\left(\Omega_{jk}(x) - \frac{\partial O_j(x)}{\partial x^l} f_k^l\right) = [U_k, O_j(x)]} \tag{36}$$

These are the conditions imposed on the field variables $O_j(x)$.

For a translation in space–time, (29) and (36), plus the fact that then $\Omega_{jk} = 0$, will give ($U_\nu \equiv P_\nu$):

$$-i\, \frac{\partial O_i(x)}{\partial x^\nu} = [P_\nu, O_i(x)] \tag{37}$$

where P_ν is the energy–momentum vector (17).

For a homogenous proper Lorentz transformation, (28) and:

$$\begin{aligned} \Omega_{ij} &\to \Omega_{i;\lambda\nu}(x) = D_{ij;\lambda\nu} O_j(x), \\ U_i &\to U_{\lambda\nu} = -M_{\lambda\nu} \end{aligned}$$

will yield:

$$i\left[D_{ij;\lambda\nu}O_j(x) - \frac{\partial O_i(x)}{\partial x^k}(\delta^k_\lambda g_{\nu\alpha} - \delta^k_\lambda g_{\lambda\alpha})\,x^\alpha\right] = [O_i(x), M_{\lambda\nu}] \quad (38)$$

where $M_{\lambda\nu}$ is the angular momentum tensor (19).

The physical meaning of (37) and (38) will be transparent in momentum space.

1.3 EMISSION AND ABSORPTION OPERATORS OF FREE FIELDS

The free field variables must satisfy the equation:

$$(\Box + m^2)\,O(x) = 0 \quad (39)$$

where:

$$\Box = g^{\mu\nu}\frac{\partial}{\partial x^\mu}\frac{\partial}{\partial x^\nu}.$$

We therefore define $O(p)\,\delta(p^2 - m^2)$ as the covariant Fourier transform of $O(x)$:

$$O(x) = \frac{1}{(2\pi)^{3/2}}\int d^4p\, e^{-ipx}\,O(p)\,\delta(p^2 - m^2); \quad px = p^\lambda x_\lambda. \quad (40)$$

$O(x)$ satisfies (39) because $(p^2 - m^2)\,\delta(p^2 - m^2) = 0$.

We separate $O(x)$ and $O(p)$ into a positive frequency and a negative frequency part:

$$O(x) = O^{(+)}(x) + O^{(-)}(x),$$

$$O(p) = O^{(+)}(p) + O^{(-)}(p) \quad (41)$$

where

$$O^{(+)}(p) = O(p)\,\tfrac{1}{2}(1 + \operatorname{sgn} p^0)$$

$$O^{(-)}(p) = O(p)\,\tfrac{1}{2}(1 - \operatorname{sgn} p^0). \quad (42)$$

As p is a time like four vector, $\operatorname{sgn} p^0$, defined by:

$$\operatorname{sgn} p^0 = \begin{cases} 1 & \text{for } p^0 > 0 \\ -1 & \text{for } p^0 < 0 \end{cases} \quad (43)$$

is invariant under proper orthochronous Lorentz transformations.

By performing the integration over p^0, it is clear that $O(x)$ can be written as an integral over the 3-dimensional momentum space.

$$O(x) = \int \frac{1}{(2\pi)^{3/2}} d^3p \, \{O^{(+)}(\mathbf{p}) \, e^{-ipx} + O^{(-)}(\mathbf{p}) \, e^{ipx}\}$$

where now:

$$O^{(+)}(\mathbf{p}) = \frac{1}{2p^0} O(\mathbf{p}),$$

$$O^{(-)}(\mathbf{p}) = \frac{1}{2p^0} O(-\mathbf{p}),$$

$$p^0 = +(\mathbf{p}^2 + m^2)^{1/2}.$$

Note that $O^{(+)}(\mathbf{p})$ and $O^{(-)}(\mathbf{p})$ depend on the 3-dimensional vector $\mathbf{p}$. One may define

$$A(\mathbf{p}) = \sqrt{2p^0} \, O^{(+)}(\mathbf{p})$$

$$B^+(\mathbf{p}) = \sqrt{2p^0} \, O^{(-)}(\mathbf{p})$$

where now B^+ is the *hermitian conjugate* of B, so that:

$$O(x) = \frac{1}{(2\pi)^{3/2}} \int \frac{d^3p}{\sqrt{2p^0}} \{A(\mathbf{p}) \, e^{-ipx} + B^+(\mathbf{p}) e^{ipx}\}. \tag{44}$$

$O(x)$, besides being an operator in Hilbert space, depends on spinor or tensor indices, α.

We separate out the two aspects in A and B by defining:

$$A_\alpha(\mathbf{p}) = \sum_r a\,(r, \mathbf{p}) \, u_\alpha\,(r, \mathbf{p})$$

$$B_\alpha^+(\mathbf{p}) = \sum_r b^+\,(r, \mathbf{p}) \, v_\alpha\,(r, \mathbf{p})$$

where the sum over r refers to polarization states, a and b are operators in Hilbert space, u_α and v_α are spinor or tensor functions.

Thus:

$$O_\alpha(x) = \frac{1}{(2\pi)^{3/2}} \int \frac{d^3p}{\sqrt{2p^0}} \{a\,(r, \mathbf{p}) \, u_\alpha\,(r, \mathbf{p}) \, e^{-ipx} + b^+(r, \mathbf{p}) \, v_\alpha\,(r, \mathbf{p}) \, e^{ipx}\}$$

$$O_\alpha^+(x) = \frac{1}{(2\pi)^{3/2}} \int \frac{d^3p}{\sqrt{2p_0}} \{b\,(r, \mathbf{p}) \, v_\alpha^+\,(r, \mathbf{p}) \, e^{-ipx} + a^+\,(r, \mathbf{p}) \, u_\alpha^+\,(r, \mathbf{p}) \, e^{ipx}\}$$

(45)

where summation over r is understood.

Thus for a *scalar field* $\varphi(x)$:

$$\varphi(x) = \frac{1}{(2\pi)^{3/2}} \int \frac{d^3p}{\sqrt{2p^0}} \{a(\mathbf{p})\, e^{-ipx} + b^+(\mathbf{p})\, e^{ipx}\}$$
$$\varphi^+(x) = \frac{1}{(2\pi)^{3/2}} \int \frac{d^3p}{\sqrt{2p^0}} \{b(\mathbf{p})\, e^{-ipx} + a^+(\mathbf{p})\, e^{ipx}\} \tag{46}$$

which will be hermitian for $a = b$.

For a *spinor field:*

$$\psi(x) = \frac{1}{(2\pi)^{3/2}} \int \frac{d^3p}{\sqrt{2p^0}} \{a\,(r, \mathbf{p})\, u\,(r, \mathbf{p})\, e^{-ipx} + b^+\,(r, \mathbf{p})\, v\,(r, \mathbf{p})\, e^{ipx}\}$$
$$\bar{\psi}(x) = \psi^+(x)\,\gamma^0 = \frac{1}{(2\pi)^{3/2}} \int \frac{d^3p}{\sqrt{2p^0}} \{b\,(r, \mathbf{p})\, \bar{v}\,(r, \mathbf{p})\, e^{-ipx} + a^+\,(r, \mathbf{p})\, \bar{u}\,(r, \mathbf{p})\, e^{ipx}\} \tag{47}$$

the spinor index α being omitted and where $\bar{\psi} = \psi^+\gamma^0$ and:

$$(\gamma^k p_k - m)\, u\,(r, \mathbf{p}) = 0, \qquad (\gamma^k p_k + m)\, v\,(r, \mathbf{p}) = 0$$
$$\bar{u}\,(r, \mathbf{p})\,(\gamma^k p_k - m) = 0, \qquad \bar{v}\,(r, \mathbf{p})\,(\gamma^k p_k + m) = 0. \tag{48}$$

Normalization of the u's and v's is taken as follows. First

$$u^+\,(r', \mathbf{p})\, u\,(r, \mathbf{p}) = 2p^0 \delta_{r'r}$$
$$p^0 > 0 \tag{49}$$
$$v^+\,(r', \mathbf{p})\, v\,(r, \mathbf{p}) = 2p^0 \delta_{r'r}$$

then it follows from the equations (48) that:

$$\bar{u}\,(r', \mathbf{p})\, u\,(r, \mathbf{p}) = 2m\delta_{r'r}$$
$$\bar{v}\,(r', \mathbf{p})\, v\,(r, \mathbf{p}) = -2m\delta_{r'r} \tag{49'}$$
$$v^+\,(r', -\mathbf{p})\, u\,(r, \mathbf{p}) = 0$$

For the *electromagnetic field:*

$$A_\mu(x) = \frac{1}{(2\pi)^{3/2}} \int \frac{d^3k}{\sqrt{2k^0}} \sum_\lambda e_\mu\,(\lambda, \mathbf{k})\, \{a\,(\lambda, \mathbf{k})\, e^{-ikx} + a^+\,(\lambda, \mathbf{k})\, e^{ikx}\}. \tag{50}$$

$e_\mu(\lambda, \mathbf{k})$ is the polarization vector; $k^0 = |\mathbf{k}|$.

We now wish *to show that the commutation rules* (37) *and* (38) *permit to interpret the operators* a, b *as absorption operators of particles with momentum* **p** *and* spin r, a^+, b^+ as emission operators.

That the *b*'s *refer to antiparticles* while the *a's refer to particles* follows from the commutation rules of the operators with the charge (next paragraph).

Consider (37) in the case in which O(x) is a spinor field $\psi(x)$. We have:

$$[\mathrm{P}_\nu, a\,(r, \mathbf{p})]\, u\,(r, \mathbf{p}) = -p_\nu a\,(r, \mathbf{p})\, u\,(r, \mathbf{p})$$
$$[\mathrm{P}_\nu, b^+\,(r, \mathbf{p})]\, v\,(r, \mathbf{p}) = p_\nu b^+\,(r, \mathbf{p})\, v\,(r, \mathbf{p}). \qquad (51)$$

Let $|\Psi(\mathrm{K})\rangle$ be a state with momentum K:

$$\mathrm{P}_\nu\, |\Psi\,(\mathrm{K})\rangle = \mathrm{K}_\nu\, |\Psi\,(\mathrm{K})\rangle$$

the K_ν being numbers. We then have:

$$[\mathrm{P}_\nu, a\,(r, \mathbf{p})]\, |\Psi(\mathrm{K})\rangle \equiv \mathrm{P}_\nu a\,(r, \mathbf{p})\, |\Psi(\mathrm{K})\rangle - a\,(r, \mathbf{p})\, \mathrm{P}_\nu\, |\Psi\,(\mathrm{K})\rangle$$
$$= (\mathrm{P}_\nu - \mathrm{K}_\nu)\, a\,(r, \mathbf{p})\, |\Psi(\mathrm{K})\rangle$$

which should be equal, according to (51), to:

$$-p_\nu a\,(r, \mathbf{p})\, |\Psi(\mathrm{K})\rangle$$

(we got rid of $u\,(r, \mathbf{p})$ in (51) by multiplying on the left by $u^+\,(r, \mathbf{p})$ and using (49)).

So:

$$\mathrm{P}_\nu\, (a\,(r, \mathbf{p})\, |\Psi(\mathrm{K})\rangle) = (\mathrm{K}_\nu - p_\nu)\, (a\,(r, \mathbf{p})\, |\Psi(\mathrm{K})\rangle). \qquad (52)$$

Thus $a\,(r, \mathbf{p})\, |\Psi(\mathrm{K})\rangle$ is an eigenvector of P_ν with momentum $\mathrm{K} - p$, hence the operator $a\,(r, \mathbf{p})$ destroys a particle of momentum p.

For $a^+\,(r, \mathbf{p})$, the operation is creation of particle. Analogously for $b\,(r, \mathbf{p})$, $b^+\,(r, \mathbf{p})$.

With (38), one obtains for spinors:

$$[a\,(r, \mathbf{p}), M_{\lambda\nu}] = (\mathrm{S}_{\lambda\nu} + \mathrm{L}_{\lambda\nu})\, a\,(r, \mathbf{p})$$

where:

$$\mathrm{S}_{\lambda\nu} = \frac{1}{2p^0}\, u^+\, \frac{i}{4}\, (\gamma_\lambda\gamma_\nu - \gamma_\nu\gamma_\lambda)\, u\,(r, \mathbf{p}) \qquad (53)$$

$$\mathrm{L}_{\lambda\nu} = x_\lambda p_\nu - x_\nu p_\lambda$$

and thus $a\,(r, \mathbf{p})$ is also absorption of a particle with spin $\mathrm{S}_{\lambda\nu}$ and orbital angular momentum $\mathrm{L}_{\lambda\nu}$.

No we want to show that a and a^+ refer to particles, b, b^+, to antiparticles.

1.4 PARTICLE AND ANTIPARTICLE OPERATORS

Assume that the wave field operators O(x) are non-hermitian. As the lagrangian must be hermitian, it can only depend on combinations of the fields like $O^+(x)\,O(x)$. Therefore, the lagrangian will be unchanged if the fields are multiplied by an arbitrary phase factor $e^{i\alpha}$:

$$O'(x) = e^{i\alpha} O(x)$$
$$O'^+(x) = e^{-i\alpha} O^+(x). \tag{54}$$

The induced transformation in Hilbert space, U(α), will be written:

$$U(\alpha) = e^{iQ\alpha} \tag{55}$$

where Q is an hermitian operator, the charge of the field. We have:

$$O'(x) = U^+(x)\,O(x)\,U(\alpha)$$

so that for infinitesimal α:

$$(1 + i\alpha)\,O(x) = (I - iQ\alpha)\,O(x)\,(I + iQ\alpha)$$

hence

$$[O(x), Q] = O(x)$$
$$[O^+(x), Q] = -O^+(x). \tag{56}$$

That Q is the charge operator follows from classical theory where it is shown that invariance of L under gauge transformation leads to a conserved vector $j^\nu(x)$, the current:

$$j^\nu(x) = i\left\{O^*(x)\frac{\partial L}{\partial\left(\dfrac{\partial O_i^*}{\partial x^\nu}\right)} - \frac{\partial L}{\partial\left(\dfrac{\partial O_i}{\partial x^\nu}\right)}O_i(x)\right\}. \tag{57}$$

This will be taken over into quantum theory, with the normal product as the ordering criterion. Now the only, first order in j, invariants formed with $j^\nu(x)$ are $\dfrac{\partial j^\nu}{\partial x^\nu}$, which vanishes, and

$$Q = \int d\sigma_\mu j^\mu(x) = \int d^3x\, j^0(x),$$

which is the charge. This is the only one available to be put in (55).

Now suppose that O(x) is $\psi(x)$ as given by (47). We get:

$$
\begin{aligned}
[a\,(r, \mathbf{p}), \mathrm{Q}] &= a\,(r, \mathbf{p}) \\
[b^+\,(r, \mathbf{p}), \mathrm{Q}] &= b^+\,(r, \mathbf{p}) \\
[a^+\,(r, \mathbf{p}), \mathrm{Q}] &= -a^+\,(r, \mathbf{p}) \\
[b\,(r, \mathbf{p}), \mathrm{Q}] &= -b\,(r, \mathbf{p}).
\end{aligned}
\tag{58}
$$

The difference in sign in the commutation rules (58) for a^+ and b^+ gives us the clue to the interpretation. Let q be the charge of a state $|\Psi(q)\rangle$ (in units of e):

$$\mathrm{Q}\,|\Psi(q)\rangle = q\,|\Psi(q)\rangle$$

then it follows from (58) that:

$a^+\,(r, \mathbf{p})\,|\Psi(q)\rangle$ is a state with charge $q + 1$;

$b^+\,(r, \mathbf{p})\,|\Psi(q)\rangle$ is a state with charge $q - 1$.

So a, a^+ are operators which refer to *particles*, b, b^+, to *antiparticles* (with charge opposite to that of particles).

1.5 LORENTZ TRANSFORMATION OF EMISSION AND ABSORPTION OPERATORS

From (4) and (45), plus the fact that

$$\mathrm{O}'(x') = \mathrm{SO}\,(x),$$

where S is a matrix which acts on the spinor or tensor indices of O(x), as illustrated by (5), (6) and (7), we obtain:

$$
\begin{aligned}
&\int \frac{d^3p}{\sqrt{2p^0}} \sum_r \{\mathrm{U}^+ a\,(r, \mathbf{p})\,\mathrm{U} u\,(r, \mathbf{p})\,e^{-ipx'} + \mathrm{U}^+ b^+\,(r, \mathbf{p})\,\mathrm{U} v\,(r, \mathbf{p})\,e^{ipx'}\} \\
&\quad = \int \frac{d^3p}{\sqrt{2p^0}} \sum_r \{a\,(r, \mathbf{p})\,\mathrm{S} u\,(r, \mathbf{p})\,e^{-ipx} + b\,(r, \mathbf{p})\,\mathrm{S} v\,(r, \mathbf{p})\,e^{ipx}\}.
\end{aligned}
$$

Change the integration variable of the left-hand side into p', such that $p'x' = px$, note that

$$\frac{d^3p'}{p^{0\prime}} = \frac{d^3p}{p^0}$$

and $u(r, \mathbf{p}') = Su(r, \mathbf{p})$, you get:

$$\sqrt{p^{0\prime}}\, U^{+} a(r, \mathbf{p}')\, U = \sqrt{p^{0}}\, a(r, \mathbf{p}) \tag{59}$$

which holds for all emission and absorption operators.

For a pure spatial rotation:

$$R^{-1} a(r, \mathbf{p}')\, R = a(r, \mathbf{p}). \tag{60}$$

As a check, verify that the energy–momentum vector being of the form:

$$P^{\mu} = \int d^3p\, p^{\mu} \{a^{+}(r, \mathbf{p})\, a(r, \mathbf{p}) + b^{+}(r, \mathbf{p})\, b(r, \mathbf{p})\}$$

(59) gives

$$U^{+} P^{\mu} U = l^{\mu}_{\nu} P^{\nu}.$$

1.6 LAGRANGIAN, ENERGY-MOMENTUM AND CURRENT OF "CLASSICAL" FIELDS

Complex scalar field $\varphi(x)$:

$$L = g_{\mu\nu} \frac{\partial \varphi^*(x)}{\partial x_{\mu}} \frac{\partial \varphi(x)}{\partial x_{\nu}} - m^2 \varphi^*(x)\, \varphi(x)$$

$$T^{\mu\lambda} = \frac{\partial \varphi^*(x)}{\partial x_{\mu}} \frac{\partial \varphi(x)}{\partial x_{\lambda}} + \frac{\partial \varphi^*(x)}{\partial x_{\lambda}} \frac{\partial \varphi(x)}{\partial x_{\mu}} - L g^{\mu\lambda} \tag{61}$$

$$j^{\nu} = i g^{\nu\alpha} \left(\varphi^*(x) \frac{\partial \varphi(x)}{\partial x^{\alpha}} - \frac{\partial \varphi^*(x)}{\partial x^{\alpha}} \varphi(x) \right).$$

Substitution of (46) in these formulae (where one replaces hermitian conjugation $^{+}$ by complex conjugation *) gives:

$$\begin{aligned} P^{\mu} &= \int d^3k\, \{a^*(\mathbf{k})\, a(\mathbf{k}) + b(\mathbf{k})\, b^*(\mathbf{k})\}\, k^{\mu} \\ Q &= \int d^3k\, \{a^*(\mathbf{k})\, a(\mathbf{k}) - b(\mathbf{k})\, b^*(\mathbf{k})\}. \end{aligned} \tag{62}$$

Spinor field $\psi(x)$:

$$L = i\bar{\psi}(x)\, \gamma^{\mu} \frac{\partial \psi(x)}{\partial x^{\mu}} - m\bar{\psi}(x)\, \psi(x)$$

$$T^{\mu\lambda} = \frac{i}{2} g^{\alpha\mu} \left(\bar{\psi}(x)\, \gamma^{\lambda} \frac{\partial \psi(x)}{\partial x^{\alpha}} - \frac{\partial \bar{\psi}(x)}{\partial x^{\alpha}} \gamma^{\lambda} \psi(x) \right) \tag{63}$$

$$j^{\nu} = \bar{\psi}(x)\, \gamma^{\nu} \psi(x)$$

which, with (47), give:

$$P^\mu = \int d^3p \sum_r \{a^* (r, \mathbf{p})\, a (r, \mathbf{p}) - b (r, \mathbf{p})\, b^* (r, \mathbf{p})\}\, p^\mu$$

$$Q = \int d^3p \sum_r \{a^* (r, \mathbf{p})\, a (r, \mathbf{p}) + b (r, \mathbf{p})\, b^* (r, \mathbf{p})\}. \qquad (64)$$

1.7 FUNDAMENTAL COMMUTATION RULES OF THE FIELD OPERATORS. NORMAL PRODUCTS. SPIN AND STATISTICS

In (61) and (63) we have written the complex conjugate of the (classical) field variables at the left of the field variables, in x-space. If we keep this order, it is seen from (46) that in momentum space, a^* will be at the left of a, b at the left of b^*. This order is irrelevant in classical theory, where the fields are ordinary functions. In quantum theory, it is important because the fields are operators.

On the other hand, (62) shows that the energy is positive definite for scalar fields and the charge is not (this is true for boson fields). But by (64) the energy would be non-positive definite for spinor fields while the charge would be positive definite. We do not want the energy to have negative values. How can we prevent this for spinor fields?

First, we remark that in quantum theory, we want that the energy–momentum and the charge of free scalar fields be of the form:

$$P^\mu = \int d^3k\, [n_+(\mathbf{k}) + n_-(\mathbf{k})]\, k^\mu$$

$$Q = \int d^3k\, [n_+(\mathbf{k}) - n_-(\mathbf{k})] \qquad (65)$$

where $\int n_+(\mathbf{k})\, d^3k$ and $\int n_-(\mathbf{k})\, d^3k$ are operators of which the eigenvalues are non-negative integral numbers, which are, respectively, the numbers of positive and negative particles. This is obtained if we impose the following commutation rules:

$$[a(\mathbf{k}), a^+(\mathbf{k}')] = \delta (\mathbf{k} - \mathbf{k}'), \qquad (66)$$

$$[b(\mathbf{k}), b^+(\mathbf{k}')] = \delta (\mathbf{k} - \mathbf{k}'),$$

$$[a(\mathbf{k}), a(\mathbf{k}')] = [b(\mathbf{k}), b(\mathbf{k}')] = [a(\mathbf{k}), b(\mathbf{k}')] = [a(\mathbf{k}), b^+(\mathbf{k}')] = 0.$$

Then

$$n_+(\mathbf{k}) = a^+(\mathbf{k})\, a(\mathbf{k})$$

$$n_-(\mathbf{k}) = b^+(\mathbf{k})\, b(\mathbf{k}). \qquad (67)$$

Indeed, it follows from (52) that if $|\Psi(0)\rangle$ is the vacuum state ($P_\nu |\Psi(0)\rangle = 0$):

$$P_\nu (a(\mathbf{p}) |\Psi(0)\rangle) = -p_\nu (a(\mathbf{p}) |\Psi(0)\rangle)$$

and as the energy P_0 must be positive definite, then

$$a(\mathbf{p}) |\Psi_0\rangle = 0$$

for $p_0 > 0$.

From (51), one deduces that:

$$|\Psi(n_1(\mathbf{k}_1), \ldots, n_s(\mathbf{k}_s))\rangle \equiv [a^+(\mathbf{k}_1)]^{n_1} \cdots [a^+(\mathbf{k}_s)]^{n_s} |\Psi(0)\rangle$$

is a state with n_1 particles with momentum $\mathbf{k}_1, \ldots, n_s$ particles with momentum $\mathbf{k}_s$.

Application of the commutation rules (66) and of the last two equations will show in a straightforward way that:

$$\int a^+(\mathbf{k})\, a(\mathbf{k})\, d^3k\, |\Psi[n_1(\mathbf{k}_1), \ldots, n_s(\mathbf{k}_s)]\rangle$$
$$= [n_1(\mathbf{k}_1) + \cdots + n_s(\mathbf{k}_s)]\, |\Psi[n_1(\mathbf{k}_1), \ldots, n_s(\mathbf{k}_s)]\rangle.$$

However, it is also possible to impose, alternatively, the following *anticommutation* rules:

$$\{a(\mathbf{k}), a(\mathbf{k}')\}_+ \equiv a(\mathbf{k})\, a^+(\mathbf{k}') + a^+(\mathbf{k}')\, a(\mathbf{k}) = \delta(\mathbf{k} - \mathbf{k}'), \tag{68}$$
$$\{b(\mathbf{k}), b^+(\mathbf{k}')\}_+ = \delta(\mathbf{k} - \mathbf{k}')$$
$$\{a(\mathbf{k}), a(\mathbf{k}')\}_+ = \{b(\mathbf{k}), b(\mathbf{k}')\}_+ = \{a(\mathbf{k}), b(\mathbf{k}')\}_+ = \{a(\mathbf{k}), b^+(\mathbf{k}')\} = 0.$$

In this case, the number operators will have as eigenvalues only 0 and 1. Replace $a(\mathbf{k})$ by $a(r, \mathbf{k})$, $b(\mathbf{k})$ by $b(r, \mathbf{k})$ and $\delta(\mathbf{k} - \mathbf{k}')$ by $\delta_{rr'}(\mathbf{k} - \mathbf{k}')$, when there is a polarization index r.

Which quantization procedure must we adopt, (66) or (68)?

If we chose (66) for the scalar field, you see that the expression (62) will not give (65) but rather:

$$P^0 = \int d^3k\, [n_+(\mathbf{k}) + n_-(\mathbf{k})]\, k^0 + \text{infinite energy}$$

due to the δ-term in (66).

The free-field vacuum state must be the one with least energy, i.e., zero. To get rid of this infinite energy for the vacuum, we may redefine all the operators like the lagrangian, energy momentum tensor, current, etc., such as (61), (62), (63), (64), by imposing the condition that the products of field operators be *normal products*, i.e., that they be ordered by displacing the emission operators always to the left of absorption operators, the sign of the commutation or anticommutation of the operators being taken in this displacement, according to (66) or (68), but the δ-term being discarded. Represent the normal product of two operators O_1O_2 by $:O_1O_2:$.

Thus, if b, b^+, obey (66):

$$:b(\mathbf{k})\,b^+(\mathbf{k}): \;=\; b^+(\mathbf{k})\,b(\mathbf{k})\,;$$

if, however, they satisfy (68):

$$:b(\mathbf{k})\,b^+(\mathbf{k}): \;=\; -b^+(\mathbf{k})\,b(\mathbf{k})\,.$$

Let us then assume that the quantities (61), (63) are, in quantum theory, normal products. The vacuum expectation value of P^μ, Q, etc., will vanish, as required.

But now we see which quantization rule to adopt for which type of field: The scalar (and, in general, the tensor) field must obey the commutation rule (66). The spinor fields must obey the anticommutation rules (68).

Thus, (64) is:

$$\begin{aligned} P^\mu &= :\int d^3p \sum_r \{a^+(r,\mathbf{p})\,a(r,\mathbf{p}) - b(r,\mathbf{p})\,b^+(r,\mathbf{p})\}\,p^\mu: \\ &= \int d^3p \sum_r \{a^+(r,\mathbf{p})\,a(r,\mathbf{p}) + b^+(r,\mathbf{p})\,b(r,\mathbf{p})\}\,p^\mu, \\ Q &= :\int d^3p \sum_r \{a^+(r,\mathbf{p})\,a(r,\mathbf{p}) + b(r,\mathbf{p})\,b^+(r,\mathbf{p})\}: \\ &= \int d^3p \sum_r \{a^+(r,\mathbf{p})\,a(r,\mathbf{p}) - b^+(r,\mathbf{p})\,b(r,\mathbf{p})\} \end{aligned} \tag{69}$$

for spinor fields, thanks to (68).

And (62) is:

$$\begin{aligned} P^\mu &= :\int d^3k\,\{a^+(\mathbf{k})\,a(\mathbf{k}) + b(\mathbf{k})\,b^+(\mathbf{k})\}\,k^\mu: \\ &= \int d^3k\,\{a^+(\mathbf{k})\,a(\mathbf{k})\;\; b^+(\mathbf{k})\,b(\mathbf{k})\}\,k^\mu, \\ Q &= :\int d^3k\,\{a^+(\mathbf{k})\,a(\mathbf{k}) - b(\mathbf{k})\,b^+(\mathbf{k})\}: \\ &= \int d^3k\,\{a^+(\mathbf{k})\,a(\mathbf{k}) - b^+(\mathbf{k})\,b(\mathbf{k})\} \end{aligned} \tag{70}$$

for scalar fields (and in general for tensor fields, if you include a polarization variable λ), thanks to (66).

You see that the *requirement that the energy be always positive-definite* imposes that tensor fields be quantized according to (66), spinor fields, according to (68).

As the occupation numbers, eigenvalues of the integrals of (67), can be any non-negative integer, in the case (66), this corresponds to the Bose–Einstein statistics, and the tensor fields, and particles, are called *bosons*.

The occupation numbers, in the case (68), can only be 0 and 1; this corresponds to a statistics which incorporates the Pauli exclusion principle, the Fermi–Dirac statistics, and the spinor fields are accordingly *fermions*.

This connection between spin and statistics was discovered in 1940 by W. Pauli.

The exclusion principle, in case (68), results from the fact that:

$$a(r, \mathbf{p})\, a(r, \mathbf{p}) = a^+(r, \mathbf{p})\, a^+(r, \mathbf{p}) = b(r, \mathbf{p})\, b(r, \mathbf{p})$$
$$= b^+(r, \mathbf{p})\, b^+(r, \mathbf{p}) = 0.$$

If you now work back from (66) and (68), through (45), you will find the commutation rules in coordinate space:

$$[\varphi^+(x), \varphi(y)] = i\Delta(x - y); \quad [\varphi(x), \varphi(y)] = 0$$

for a scalar field;

$$[\mathrm{A}^\mu(x), \mathrm{A}^\nu(y)] = -ig^{\mu\nu}\mathrm{D}(x - y) \tag{71}$$

for the electromagnetic field;

$$\{\psi_\alpha(x), \bar{\psi}_\beta(y)\}_+ = -i\mathrm{S}_{\alpha\beta}(x - y); \quad \{\psi_\alpha(x), \psi_\beta(y)\}_+ = 0$$

for a spinor field. Here:

$$\Delta(x) = -\frac{1}{(2\pi)^3}\int \frac{d^3k}{k^0}\, e^{i\mathbf{kx}} \sin k^0 x^0,$$

$$k^0 = (\mathbf{k}^2 + m^2)^{1/2}; \quad \mathrm{D}(x) = \Delta(x) \quad \text{for } m = 0 \tag{72}$$

$$\mathrm{S}(x) = -\left(i\gamma^\mu \frac{\partial}{\partial x^\mu} + m\right)\Delta(x).$$

These functions satisfy:

$$(\Box + m^2)\,\Delta(x) = 0,$$

$(\Delta x) = 0$ for a space-like vector x,

$$\left(\frac{\partial \Delta(x)}{\partial x^0}\right)_{x^0=0} = -\delta(\mathbf{x}) \tag{73}$$

$$\left(i\gamma^\mu \frac{\partial}{\partial x^\mu} - m\right)\mathrm{S}(x) = 0$$

and are the ones which solve the Cauchy problem for free fields.

Thus the *commutation rules* (71) *hold only for field operators* which satisfy the free-field equations.

On the other hand, *the more restricted rules:*

$$[\varphi^+(x), \varphi(y)] = 0 \quad \text{for } x - y \text{ a space-like vector,}$$

$$\left[\frac{\partial}{\partial x^0}\varphi^+(x), \varphi(y)\right]_{y^0 = x^0} = -i\delta(\mathbf{x} - \mathbf{y}) \tag{74}$$

$$[\mathrm{A}^\mu(x), \mathrm{A}^\nu(y)] = 0 \quad \text{for } x - y \text{ space-like,}$$

$$\left[\frac{\partial \mathrm{A}^\mu(x)}{\partial x^0}, \mathrm{A}^\nu(y)\right]_{y^0 = x^0} = ig^{\mu\nu}\,\delta(\mathbf{x} - \mathbf{y})$$

$$\{\psi(x), \psi^+(y)\}_+ = \delta(\mathbf{x} - \mathbf{y}) \quad \text{for } x^0 = y^0$$

still *hold when there is an interaction* among the fields, which does not involve field derivatives.

1.8 INTERACTIONS

The physical processes are due to the interaction among fundamental fields. An interaction between two wave fields $O_1(x)$ and $O_2(x)$ is taken into account by adding to the two free-field lagrangians of $O_1(x)$ and $O_2(x)$, a third term L', the interaction lagrangian, which is constructed as a normal product of expressions formed with $O_1(x)$ and $O_2(x)$, in such a way that L' be hermitian and invariant under the proper Poincaré group. Further requirements may be imposed on L' for specific cases: the coupling of charged fields with the electromagnetic field must be gauge-invariant, the interaction of nucleous with pions, in the absence of electromagnetic effects, must be charge independent, the strong couplings of baryons with mesons must be, as far as we now know, invariant under space reflection, charge conjugation and time reversal, separately. The last requirement must not be imposed for weak interactions, such as the Fermi coupling among spinor fields, except for invariance under time reversal. Experiment is our guide in the choice of these impositions, as it has been, so far, for the Lorentz invariance of the theory.

The interaction lagrangian gives rise to terms in each field equation which make it depend on the other fields. The wave equations are coupled together.

We shall consider only local interactions, for which $O_1(x)$ and $O_2(x)$ are taken at the same point x, in L'.

If follows from (7) and (15) that the adjoint of a Dirac spinor field, $\bar{\psi}(x)$, transforms, under a proper Poincaré transformation, in the following way:

$$\bar{\psi}'(x') = \bar{\psi}(x)\,\mathrm{D}^{-1}. \tag{75}$$

Then, with the help of (7), (8) and (75), you will show that, if $\psi_1(x)$ and $\psi_2(x)$ are two spinor fields (representing, for example, protons and neutrons, respectively), $\bar{\psi}_1(x)\,\psi_2(x)$ is invariant with respect to the Lorentz group, a scalar S; $\bar{\psi}_1(x)\,\gamma^\mu\psi_2(x)$ is a four-vector V; $\frac{i}{2}\,\bar{\psi}_1(x)\,[\gamma^\mu,\gamma^\nu]\,\psi_2(x)$ is an anti-symmetric tensor T. It will be shown in the next chapter that, in addition, the following forms, $\bar{\psi}_1(x)\,\gamma^\mu\gamma^5\psi_2(x)$ and $i\bar{\psi}_1\,(x)\,\gamma^5\psi_2\,(x)$ are a pseudovector (or axial vector) A and pseudoscalar P, respectively, because under space reflections they behave as such (here $\gamma^5 = i\gamma^0\gamma^1\gamma^2\gamma^3$).

Thus we have the table

Tensor character	Bilinear form	Hermitian conjugate
S	$\bar{\psi}_1(x)\,\psi_2(x)$	$\bar{\psi}_2(x)\,\psi_1(x)$
V	$\bar{\psi}_1(x)\,\gamma^\mu\psi_2(x)$	$\bar{\psi}_2(x)\,\gamma^\mu\psi_1(x)$
T	$\frac{i}{2}\bar{\psi}_1(x)\,[\gamma^\mu,\gamma^\nu]\,\psi_2(x)$	$\frac{i}{2}\bar{\psi}_2(x)\,[\gamma^\mu,\gamma^\nu]\,\psi_1(x)$
A	$\bar{\psi}_1(x)\,\gamma^\mu\gamma^5\psi_2(x)$	$\bar{\psi}_2(x)\,\gamma^\mu\gamma^5\psi_1(x)$
P	$i\bar{\psi}_1(x)\,\gamma^5\psi_2(x)$	$i\bar{\psi}_2(x)\,\gamma^5\psi_1(x)$

(76)

Remember that we have chosen:

$$(\gamma^\mu)^+ = \gamma^0\gamma^\mu\gamma^0, \quad (\gamma^5)^+ = \gamma^5$$
$$\gamma^5 = i\gamma^0\gamma^1\gamma^2\gamma^3.$$

The following are some examples of interacting fields:

1.8.1 Charged fermions and electromagnetic field

$$L = L_1 + L_2 + L',$$

$$L_1 = -\frac{1}{2}:\frac{\partial A^\mu(x)}{\partial x^\nu}\,\frac{\partial A_\mu(x)}{\partial x_\nu}:$$

$$L_2 =: i\bar{\psi}(x)\,\gamma^\mu\,\frac{\partial\psi(x)}{\partial x^\mu} - m\bar{\psi}(x)\,\psi(x): \tag{77}$$

$$L' = -e:\bar{\psi}(x)\,\gamma^\mu\psi\,(x)\,A_\mu(x):$$

The field equations of motion are:

$$\left\{\gamma^\mu \left(i\frac{\partial}{\partial x^\mu} - eA_\mu(x)\right) - m\right\} \psi(x) = 0$$

$$\Box A^\mu(x) = e\bar{\psi}(x)\gamma^\mu\psi(x) \tag{78}$$

and the Lorentz supplementary condition on the state vectors:

$$\frac{\partial A_\mu^{(+)}(x)}{\partial x_\mu}\Psi = 0. \tag{79}$$

The equations are obtained in the following way. With L, one obtains $T^{\mu\nu}$ and P^ν. With P^ν, one uses equation (37), where $O_i(x)$ is $\psi(x)$ and $A^\mu(x)$. To calculate the commutator in (37), one needs commutation rules for the fields. These cannot be (71) because they would lead to free field equations. The commutation rules (74), which refer to fields taken at the same time, and the additional condition that $\psi(x)$ and $A_\mu(y)$ commute for $y^0 = x^0$, will give the equations (78).

Commutation rules (74) can be written in a more general fashion, if σ designates a space-like surface and $F(x)$ is an arbitrary function:

$$\begin{aligned}
&\int d\sigma_\mu\, [\varphi^+(x), \varphi(y)] = 0, \quad \text{for } y \text{ in } \sigma;\\
&\int d\sigma_\mu \left[\frac{\partial\varphi^+(x)}{\partial x_\mu}, \varphi(y)\right] F(x) = -iF(y), \quad y \text{ in } \sigma;\\
&\int d\sigma_\mu\, [A^\lambda(x), A^\nu(y)] = 0, \quad y \text{ in } \sigma;\\
&\int d\sigma^\mu \left[\frac{\partial A^\lambda(x)}{\partial x_\mu}, A^\nu(y)\right] F(x) = ig^{\lambda\nu}F(y), \quad y \text{ in } \sigma;\\
&\int d\sigma_\mu\, \{\psi(x), \bar{\psi}(y)\gamma^\mu\}_+ F(x) = F(y), \quad y \text{ in } \sigma;\\
&\int d\sigma_\mu\, \{\psi(x), \psi(y)\} = 0, \quad y \text{ in } \sigma;\\
&\int d\sigma_\mu\, [A^\mu(x), \psi(y)] = 0, \quad y \text{ in } \sigma.
\end{aligned} \tag{80}$$

Equations (78) give the time development of the field operators and this constitutes the so-called *Heisenberg representation or picture*, in which the state vectors $|\Psi\rangle$ are regarded as fixed in time.

(77) is gauge-invariant, i.e. invariant under the transformations:

$$\begin{aligned}
A'_\mu(x) &= A_\mu(x) + \frac{\partial\Lambda(x)}{\partial x^\mu}\\
\psi'(x) &= e^{ie\Lambda(x)}\psi(x)\\
\bar{\psi}'(x) &= e^{-ie\Lambda(x)}\bar{\psi}(x)
\end{aligned} \tag{81}$$

where $\Lambda(x)$ is an ordinary function which obeys the equation $\Box\Lambda(x) = 0$.

You will notice that L' was made out of the contraction of $A_\mu(x)$ with $\bar{\psi}(x)\,\gamma^\mu\psi\,(x)$, which guarantees its relativistic invariance. A contraction of $\bar{\psi}\gamma^\mu\gamma^5\psi\,(x)$ with $A_\mu(x)$ would destroy gauge invariance (under (81)). Thus, it seems that the gauge-invariance requirement leads to a space reflection invariant coupling.

The fact that the electromagnetic effects are described by the interaction (77), without the need of an additional term in the lagrangian, of the form

$$\frac{i}{2}\,\bar{\psi}(x)\,[\gamma^\mu, \gamma^\nu]\,\psi(x)\,F_{\mu\nu}(x), \quad \text{where} \quad F_{\mu\nu}(x) = \frac{\partial A_\mu}{\partial x^\nu} - \frac{\partial A_\nu}{\partial x^\mu}$$

(such a term results in the second order equation), has led Gell-Mann to propose the *principle of minimal electromagnetic interaction*, which restricts all direct electromagnetic couplings to those with $A_\mu(x)$ in the lagrangian.

1.8.2 Nucleons and pions. Charge independence and charge symmetry

Positive and negative pions are described by a non-hermitian pseudoscalar field operator $\varphi(x)$, neutral pions by a hermitian pseudoscalar field $\varphi_3(x)$. The proton field is a Dirac spinor $\psi_p(x)$, the neutron field, another Dirac spinor $\psi_n(x)$.

The lagrangian is:

$$L = L_n + L_\pi + L'$$

$$L_n = :i\bar{\psi}_p(x)\gamma^\mu \frac{\partial\psi_p(x)}{\partial x^\mu} - M\bar{\psi}_p(x)\,\psi_p(x):$$

$$+ :i\bar{\psi}_n(x)\,\gamma^\mu \frac{\partial\psi_n(x)}{\partial x^\mu} - M\psi_n(x)\,\psi_n(x):$$

$$L_\pi = -:\left(\mu^2\varphi^+(x)\,\varphi(x) - \frac{\partial\varphi^+(x)}{\partial x^\mu}\frac{\partial\varphi\,(x)}{\partial x_\mu}\right): \tag{82}$$

$$-\frac{1}{2}:\left(\mu^2\varphi_3^2(x) - \frac{\partial\varphi_3(x)}{\partial x^\mu}\frac{\partial\varphi_3(x)}{\partial x_\mu}\right):$$

$$L' = ig_c:[(\bar{\psi}_p(x)\,\gamma^5\psi_n(x))\,\varphi(x) + (\bar{\psi}_n(x)\,\gamma^5\psi_p(x))\,\varphi^+(x)]:$$

$$+\, ig_p:\bar{\psi}_p(x)\gamma^5\psi_p(x)\,\varphi_3(x): + ig_n:\bar{\psi}_n(x)\gamma^5\psi_n(x)\,\varphi_3(x):$$

with an obvious meaning for the different terms and the coupling constants g_c, g_p, g_n; the g_c terms couple charged pions with transitions between neutron and proton states; the g_p and g_n terms couple neutral pions with proton and neutron states respectively; μ is the pion mass, M the mass of neutron and proton, assumed equal.

The *charge-independent theory*, first proposed by Kemmer, makes:

$$\frac{1}{\sqrt{2}} g_c = g_p = -g_n \equiv g\,. \tag{83}$$

Introduce an 8-component spinor:

$$\psi(x) = \begin{pmatrix} \psi_p(x) \\ \psi_n(x) \end{pmatrix} \tag{84}$$

and the isobaric spin matrices τ_1, τ_2, τ_3 such that:

$$\tau_1\psi(x) = \begin{pmatrix} \psi_n(x) \\ \psi_p(x) \end{pmatrix}, \quad \tau_2\psi(x) = \begin{pmatrix} -i\psi_n(x) \\ i\psi_p(x) \end{pmatrix}, \tag{85}$$

$$\tau_3\psi(x) = \begin{pmatrix} \psi_p(x) \\ -\psi_n(x) \end{pmatrix}.$$

Then:

$$\tau_+ = \frac{1}{\sqrt{2}}(\tau_1 + i\tau_2), \quad \tau_- = \frac{1}{\sqrt{2}}(\tau_1 - i\tau_2) \tag{86}$$

give:

$$\psi(x)\,\tau_+\Gamma\psi(x) = \sqrt{2}\,\bar{\psi}_p(x)\Gamma\psi_n(x)$$

$$\bar{\psi}(x)\,\tau_-\Gamma\psi(x) = \sqrt{2}\,\bar{\psi}_n(x)\Gamma\psi_p(x)$$

where Γ is any of the 16 γ-matrices which act on $\psi(x)$ as follows:

$$\Gamma\psi(x) = \begin{pmatrix} \Gamma\psi_p(x) \\ \Gamma\psi_n(x) \end{pmatrix}, \quad [\Gamma, \tau_i] = 0. \tag{87}$$

One then finds, with (83):

$$L' = ig : \sum_{i=1}^{3} \bar{\psi}(x)\,\tau_i\gamma^5\psi(x)\,\varphi_i(x) : \tag{88}$$

where:

$$\varphi(x) = \frac{1}{\sqrt{2}}(\varphi_1(x) - i\varphi_2(x)) \tag{89}$$

and $\varphi_1(x)$ and $\varphi_2(x)$ are hermitian.

We see that now $\psi(x)$, as defined by (84), has two kinds of spinor indices, one $\alpha = 1, 2, 3, 4$, defines it as a 4-component Dirac spinor, the other $i = 1, 2$, defines it as a 2-component spinor in the *isobaric spin space*. The matrices τ_1, τ_2, τ_3 are the infinitesimal operators which generate a rotation in this space. The pseudoscalar field has an isobaric spin index $i = 1, 2, 3$, which defines it as a 3-vector in the isobaric spin space. The coupling (88) is Lorentz-invariant and, in addition, *invariant under rotations in the isobaric spin space*. This is the requirement of charge independence, which holds for (83).

Thus we can write (82) in a more compact form:

$$L = L_N + L_\pi + L',$$

$$\left.\begin{aligned} L_N &= :\bar{\psi}(x)\left(i\gamma^\alpha \frac{\partial}{\partial x^\alpha} - M\right)\psi(x): \\ L_\pi &= -\frac{1}{2}\sum_{i=1}^{3} :\left(\mu^2\varphi_i^2(x) - \frac{\partial\varphi_i(x)}{\partial x^\alpha}\frac{\partial\varphi_i(x)}{\partial x_\alpha}\right): \\ L' &= ig:\sum_{i=1}^{3}\bar{\psi}(x)\,\tau_i\gamma^5\psi(x)\,\varphi_i(x): \end{aligned}\right\} \qquad (82')$$

A *special rotation* in the isobaric spin space is the one around the first axis in this space by an angle π. The transformed pion field $\varphi_i'(x)$ will be:

$$\varphi_1'(x) = \varphi_1(x), \quad \varphi_2'(x) = -\varphi_2(x), \quad \varphi_3'(x) = -\varphi_3(x) \qquad (90)$$

One then sees that the nucleon field $\psi(x)$ transforms in the following way:

$$\psi'(x) = \tau_1\psi(x). \qquad (91)$$

In terms of $\varphi(x)$, (89), $\psi_p(x)$ and $\psi_n(x)$, (84), one gets:

$$\begin{aligned} \varphi'(x) &= \varphi^+(x) \\ \varphi^{+\prime}(x) &= \varphi(x) \\ \psi_p'(x) &= \psi_n(x) \\ \psi_n'(x) &= \psi_p(x). \end{aligned} \qquad (92)$$

This is the so-called *charge symmetry* operation, under which protons are replaced by neutrons, neutrons by protons, and positive and negative pions are interchanged. Nuclei have this symmetry, as known from the fact that the energies of the ground states of two mirror nuclei are equal, except for a small amount due to the coulomb energy of protons.

While a charge-independent theory is automatically charge-symmetric, the reverse is not true, as is obvious by the above considerations.

1.8.3 Fermi interactions

This is the coupling which we want in order to describe processes like the muon beta-decay:

$$\mu^- \to v + e + \bar{\nu}$$

the muon decays into a μ-neutrino ν', an electron and an e-antineutrino.

With the help of the table (76), we can construct an interaction lagrangian suitable for this purpose:

$$\begin{aligned} L' =\, :&(\bar{\psi}_{v'}\psi_\mu)\,(\bar{\psi}_e\,[C_s - C_s'\gamma^5]\,\psi_\nu) \\ &+ (\bar{\psi}_{v'}\gamma^\mu\psi_\mu)\,(\bar{\psi}_e\gamma_\mu\,[C_V - C_V'\gamma^5]\,\psi_\nu) \\ &+ \left(\bar{\psi}_{v'}\,\frac{i}{2}\,[\gamma^\mu, \gamma^\nu]\,\psi_\mu\right)\left(\bar{\psi}_e\,\frac{i}{2}\,[\gamma_\mu, \gamma_\nu]\,(C_T - C_T'\gamma^5)\right)\psi_\nu \\ &+ (\bar{\psi}_{v'}\gamma^\mu\gamma^5\psi_\mu)\,(\bar{\psi}_e\gamma_\mu\gamma^5\,(C_A - C_A'\gamma^5)\,\psi^\nu) \\ &+ (\bar{\psi}_{v'}i\gamma^5\psi_\mu)\,(\bar{\psi}_e i\gamma^5\,(C_P - C_P'\gamma^5)\,\psi_\nu) \\ &+ (\bar{\psi}_\mu\psi_{v'})\,(\bar{\psi}_\nu\,(C_S^* + C_S'^*\gamma^5)\,\psi_e) \qquad (93) \\ &+ (\bar{\psi}_\mu\gamma^\mu\psi_{v'})\,(\bar{\psi}_\nu\gamma_\mu\,(C_V^* - C_V'^*\gamma^5)\,\psi_e) \\ &+ \left(\bar{\psi}_\mu\,\frac{i}{2}\gamma^\mu, \gamma^\nu]\,\psi_{v'}\right)\left(\bar{\psi}_\nu\,\frac{i}{2}\,[\gamma_\mu, \gamma_\nu]\,C_T^* + C_T'^*\gamma^5)\,\psi_e\right) \\ &+ (\bar{\psi}_\mu\gamma^\mu\gamma^5\psi_{v'})\,(\bar{\psi}_\nu\gamma_\mu\gamma^5\,(C_A^* - C_A'^*\gamma^5)\,\psi_e) \\ &+ (\bar{\psi}_\mu i\gamma^5\psi_{v'})\,(\bar{\psi}_\nu i\gamma^5\,(C_P^* + C_P'^*\gamma^5)\,\psi_e): \end{aligned}$$

L' is hermitian and Lorentz invariant. Invariance under space reflection, charge conjugation and time reversal depends on the choice of the coupling constants C and C′, as will be seen in the next chapters. The last five terms are the hermitian conjugate of the first five and describe the inverse process:

$$\nu' \to \mu^- + \bar{e} + \nu.$$

ν is the neutrino associated to the electron. The fields are taken at the same point x.

1.8.4 Pions and the electromagnetic field

In this case, the interaction lagrangian is:

$$L' = ie{:}A^{\mu}(x)\left(\varphi^{+}(x)\frac{\partial\varphi}{\partial x^{\mu}} - \frac{\partial\varphi^{+}}{\partial x^{\mu}}\varphi(x)\right) - e^{2}A^{\mu}(x)\,A_{\mu}(x)\,\varphi^{+}(x)\,\varphi(x){:} \quad (94)$$

1.8.5. Current-current effective lagrangian

Actually, it is not known that the nucleons are only part of a family of baryons which group themselves into multiplets: an octet of spin-$\frac{1}{2}$ particles, namely, the neutron and proton, the Λ-particle, the three Σ's and the two cascade particles; and a spin-$\frac{3}{2}$ decuplet, formed of four resonances (the Δ's), three y^*-resonances, two cascade resonances and the SL-particle.

Mesons are grouped under an octet and a singlet with zero spin—location of the pions and kaons—and similarly an octet and a singlet with spin one. Other resonances may hopefully be classified as orbital-excited states of suitable configurations of quarks (see J.J.J. Kokkedee, *The quark model*, W.A. Benjamin Inc., New York, 1969).

In view of the strong interactions among baryons and mesons—collectively called hadrons—it is not meaningful to write for these particles interaction lagrangians similar, for instance, to equation (93) (which is, however, valid for particles which have no strong interactions). The effective interaction lagrangian for weak interactions has the form of a coupling between currents:

$$L = \frac{G}{2\sqrt{z}}\left(j^{+}_{\mu}j^{\mu} + j^{\mu}j^{+}_{\mu}\right)$$

where $j^{\mu} = j^{\mu}_{h} + j^{\mu}_{l}$ is a sum of a hadronic current and a current for leptons (electron, muon and associated neutrinos). Lagrangian (93) is that part of L containing the coupling $j^{+}_{\lambda l}j^{\lambda}_{l}$ and it is known that all C's are zero except $C_V = C_A = C'_V = C'_A = \dfrac{G}{2\sqrt{z}}$. Hadronic currents refer to baryons and mesons and their matrix elements between incoming and outgoing particle states are expressed in terms of form factors, in- and out-fields and available variables such as momenta and γ-matrices. (See F.J. Low, *Symmetries and elementary particles*, Gordon and Breach, New York, 1967; S.L. Adler and R.F. Dashen, *Current algebras*, W. Benjamin Inc., New York, 1968.)

CHAPTER 2

Space Reflection and Parity: Bose Fields

2.1 PARITY IN NON-RELATIVISTIC QUANTUM MECHANICS

Let:

$$-\frac{1}{2m}\nabla^2\psi(\mathbf{x}, t) + V(r)\,\psi(\mathbf{x}, t) = i\,\frac{\partial\psi(\mathbf{x}, t)}{\partial t} \tag{95}$$

be the Schrödinger equation of a particle which moves in a central field in which it has a time-independent potential energy $V(r)$, $r = |\mathbf{x}|$.

It is well-known that the stationary states of this system are specified by three quantum numbers n, l, m and the corresponding solutions of the wave equation are

$$\psi_{nlm}(\mathbf{x}, t) = R_{nl}(r)\,Y_{lm}(\theta, \varphi)\,e^{-iE_n t} \tag{96}$$

where r, θ, φ are the polar coordinates, $R_{nl}(r)$ is the radial wave function, $Y_{lm}(\theta, \varphi)$ are the spherical harmonics, E_n, the energy of the state. Normalization coefficients are included in the functions.

Let us now introduce new, space-reflected coordinates:

$$\mathbf{x}' = -\mathbf{x}, \quad t' = t \tag{97}$$

and look for the transformed wave functions

$$\psi'(\mathbf{x}', t') = P\psi(\mathbf{x}', t) \tag{98}$$

which satisfy the same equation in the new system, as $\psi(\mathbf{x}, t)$ does in the old one:

$$-\frac{1}{2m}\nabla'^2\psi'(\mathbf{x}', t') + V'(r')\,\psi'(\mathbf{x}', t') = i\,\frac{\partial\psi'(\mathbf{x}', t')}{\partial t'}\,. \tag{99}$$

Because:

$$V'(r') = V(r), \quad \nabla'^2 = \nabla^2, \quad t' = t$$

we see that the coefficients of ψ' in (99) are the same as those of ψ in (95). We can therefore write:

$$\psi'(\mathbf{x}', t) \equiv \mathrm{P}\psi(\mathbf{x}', t) = \varepsilon\psi(\mathbf{x}, t)$$

where ε is an indeterminate phase factor:

$$\varepsilon\varepsilon^* = 1.$$

Thus:

$$\mathrm{P}\psi(\mathbf{x}, t) = \varepsilon\psi(-\mathbf{x}, t).$$

But by a well-known property of $\mathrm{Y}_{lm}(\theta, \varphi)$:

$$\psi_{nlm}(-\mathbf{x}, t) = (-1)^l \psi_{nlm}(\mathbf{x}, t)$$

So:

$$\mathrm{P}\psi_{nlm}(\mathbf{x}, t) = (-1)^l \varepsilon\psi_{nlm}(\mathbf{x}, t). \tag{100}$$

We see that, under the parity operation P (in the space of wave functions), the wave function of a state with angular momentum quantum number l *acquires a phase* $(-1)^l$ *relative to that of the S-state wave function*. This phase is called the *parity of the state.*

We also see that the complex number of modulus one, ε, is indeterminate, as a phase factor of the (complex) wave function is. *The relative parity of a state with respect to the S-state is well determined and independent of* ε, *namely* $(-1)^l$.

One may, however, *arbitrarily* wish to attribute an even parity to the S-state and thus choose $\varepsilon = 1$. As $\mathrm{V}(r)$ is even, it is conventional to say that the non-relativistic spinless particle described by (95) has an *even intrinsic parity*, it is a scalar particle.

The choice $\varepsilon = -1$ gives an odd parity to the S-state and the particle is accordingly called a pseudoscalar particle, i.e., it has an *odd intrinsic parity.*

2.2 PARITY IN QUANTUM FIELD THEORY

The proper and orthochronous Lorentz transformations of fields and state vectors are determined by the requirement that the coupled field equations, or the complete lagrangian, be invariant under such transformations. It follows from (3), (4) and (5), (6), (7) that one has in this case:

$$\langle \Psi' | \mathrm{O}_i'(x') | \Psi' \rangle = \mathrm{A}_{ij} \langle \Psi | \mathrm{O}_j(x) | \Psi \rangle \tag{101}$$

where A is a matrix which acts on the spinor or tensor index i of the operator $\mathrm{O}(x)$.

Thus, for a relativistically invariant operator $F\left(O_i(x), \dfrac{\partial O_i(x)}{\partial x^\mu}\right)$ formed with the operator and its derivatives, such as the lagrangian, one has:

$$\left\langle \Psi' \middle| F'\left(O_i'(x'), \frac{\partial O_i'(x')}{\partial x^{\mu'}}\right) \middle| \Psi' \right\rangle = \left\langle \Psi \middle| F\left(O_i(x), \frac{\partial O_i(x)}{\partial x^\mu}\right) \middle| \Psi \right\rangle. \tag{102}$$

From (101) and: either $|\Psi'\rangle = |\Psi\rangle$, $O'(x) = U^+O(x)U$ in the Heisenberg–Lorentz transformation, or $|\Psi'\rangle = U|\Psi\rangle$ and $O'(x) = O(x)$ in the Schrödinger–Lorentz transformation, we obtain:

$$UO(x)U^{-1} = A^{-1}O(L^{-1}x). \tag{103}$$

We shall assume the same relations for the space reflections and call P the parity operation in Hilbert space and S the matrix which acts on the spinor or tensor indices, R the special case of the 4-vector indices:

$$PO(x)P^{-1} = sS^{-1}O(R^{-1}x) \tag{14}$$

$$R = \begin{pmatrix} 1 & 0 & 0 & 0 \\ 0 & -1 & 0 & 0 \\ 0 & 0 & -1 & 0 \\ 0 & 0 & 0 & -1 \end{pmatrix} \tag{105}$$

and s is a phase factor, $s^* \cdot s = 1$, also allowed in (103).

2.3 PARITY TRANSFORMED OF SPINLESS FIELDS

Consider a *hermitian* spinless field $\varphi_0(x)$. Then S must be the identity. (104) and (105) give:

$$P\varphi_0(x)P^{-1} = s\varphi_0(-\mathbf{x}, x_0). \tag{106}$$

If the free-field lagrangian is invariant under P:

$$s^2 = 1. \tag{107}$$

We call the field *scalar* for $s = +1$, *pseudoscalar* for $s = -1$, if the vacuum state $|\Psi_0\rangle$ is even under P.

Let $\varphi(x)$ be a *non-hermitian* spinless field. Then:

$$\begin{aligned} P\varphi(x)P^{-1} &= s\varphi(-\mathbf{x}, x^0) \\ P\varphi^+(x)P^{-1} &= s^* \cdot \varphi^+(-\mathbf{x}, x^0) \end{aligned} \tag{108}$$

Invariance of the free-field lagrangian imposes that s is a complex number of modulus 1:

$$s^* \cdot s = 1. \tag{109}$$

P is a unitary operator: it conserves the commutation rules (71) for $\varphi(x)$.

(46) and (108) will give you the transformed of the emission and absorption operators:

$$\begin{aligned} \mathrm{P}a(\mathbf{k})\,\mathrm{P}^{-1} &= s \cdot a(-\mathbf{k}) \\ \mathrm{P}b(\mathbf{k})\,\mathrm{P}^{-1} &= s^* \cdot b(-\mathbf{k}) \\ \mathrm{P}a^+(\mathbf{k})\,\mathrm{P}^{-1} &= s^* \cdot a^+(-\mathbf{k}) \\ \mathrm{P}b^+(\mathbf{k})\,\mathrm{P}^{-1} &= s \cdot b^+(-\mathbf{k}). \end{aligned} \tag{110}$$

The amplitude of a state with n particles is:

$$|\Psi_n\rangle = \int \mathrm{F}_n(\mathbf{k}_1, \ldots, \mathbf{k}_n) \cdot a^+(\mathbf{k}_1) \cdots a^+(\mathbf{k}_n)\,|\Psi_0\rangle \cdot d^3k_1 \ldots d^3k_n \tag{111}$$

where $|\Psi_0\rangle$ is the vacuum state.

The convention that the latter is even:

$$\mathrm{P}\,|\Psi_0\rangle = |\Psi_0\rangle$$

leads to, because of (110):

$$\mathrm{P}\,|\Psi_n\rangle = (s^*)^n \cdot \int \mathrm{F}_n(-\mathbf{k}_1, \ldots, -\mathbf{k}_n) \cdot a^+(\mathbf{k}_1) \cdots a^+(\mathbf{k}_n)\,|\Psi_0\rangle\, d^3k_1 \cdots d^3k_n$$

so that, defining PF_n by:

$$\mathrm{P}\,|\Psi_n\rangle = \int (\mathrm{PF}_n(\mathbf{k}_1, \cdots, \mathbf{k}_n)) \cdot a^+(\mathbf{k}_1) \ldots a^+(\mathbf{k}_n)\,|\Psi_0\rangle\, d^3k_1 \cdots d^3k_n$$

we have:

$$\mathrm{P} \cdot \mathrm{F}_n(\mathbf{k}_1, \ldots, \mathbf{k}_n) = (s^*)^n \cdot \mathrm{F}_n(-\mathbf{k}_1, \ldots, -\mathbf{k}_n).$$

The wave function of the n particles in coordinate space

$$\Phi(\mathbf{x}_1, \ldots, \mathbf{x}_n),$$

Fourier-transformed of F_n:

$$\mathrm{F}_n(\mathbf{k}_1, \ldots, \mathbf{k}_n) = \frac{1}{(2\pi)^{3/2}} \cdot \int e^{i(\mathbf{k}_1\mathbf{x}_1 + \cdots + \mathbf{k}_n\mathbf{x}_n)} \cdot \Phi_n(\mathbf{x}_1, \ldots, \mathbf{x}_n)\, d^3x_1 \cdots d^3x_n$$

will be transformed in the following way:

$$\mathrm{P}\Phi_n(\mathbf{x}_1, \ldots, \mathbf{x}_n) = (s^*)^n \cdot \Phi_n(-\mathbf{x}_1, \ldots, -\mathbf{x}_n). \tag{112}$$

The same result holds when the particles interact with an even static potential. If there are n_1 particles with angular momentum $l_1, \ldots, n_j$ with angular momentum l_j, then:

$$\Phi(-\mathbf{x}_1, \ldots, -\mathbf{x}_n) = (-1)^{n_1 l_1 + \ldots + n_j l_j} \cdot \Phi(\mathbf{x}_1, \ldots, \mathbf{x}_n).$$

As in II.1, we make the convention to call the particles scalar if s is arbitrarily chosen $+1$, pseudoscalar if $s = -1$. The parity of a n-scalar-meson-state is $(-1)^{n_1 l_1 + \cdots + n_j l_j}$, that of an n-pseudoscalar meson state is $(-1)^{n_1 l_1 + \cdots + n_j l_j + n}$.

2.4 PARITY OF PHOTONS

In classical electrodynamics, one assumes that the charge density is invariant under space reflection:

$$\varrho'(x) = \varrho(-\mathbf{x}, x^0).$$

It follows that charge-conservation invariance:

$$\nabla \cdot \mathbf{j} + \frac{\partial \varrho}{\partial t} = 0$$

imposes:

$$j'(x) = -j(-\mathbf{x}, x^0).$$

Invariance of Maxwell's equations will then lead to a polar electric field $\mathbf{E}$ and an axial magnetic field $\mathbf{H}$:

$$\mathbf{E}'(x) = -\mathbf{E}(-\mathbf{x}, x^0)$$

$$\mathbf{H}'(x) = \mathbf{H}(-\mathbf{x}, x^0)$$

hence

$$\mathbf{A}'(x) = -\mathbf{A}(-\mathbf{x}, x^0)$$

$$\mathrm{A}_0'(x) = \mathrm{A}_0(-\mathbf{x}, x^0).$$

We want these relations to hold in quantum theory, consistently with $\mathrm{S} \equiv \mathrm{R}$, $s = 1$, in (194), (105):

$$\mathrm{P}\mathbf{A}(x)\,\mathrm{P}^{-1} = -\mathbf{A}(-\mathbf{x}, x^0)$$

$$\mathrm{P}\mathrm{A}_0(x)\,\mathrm{P}^{-1} = \mathrm{A}_0(-\mathbf{x}, x^0). \qquad (113)$$

The Fourier development (50) and the supplementary condition (79) give:

$$k^\mu \sum_\lambda e_\mu(\lambda, \mathbf{k})\, a(\lambda, \mathbf{k})\, |\Psi\rangle = 0$$

and this, together with the choice:

$$\begin{aligned} k &= |\mathbf{k}|\,(1, 0, 0, 1) \\ e^\mu(0, \mathbf{k}) &= (1, 0, 0, 0) \\ e^\mu(1, \mathbf{k}) &= (0, 1, 0, 0) \\ e^\mu(2, \mathbf{k}) &= (0, 0, 1, 0) \\ e^\mu(3, \mathbf{k}) &= (0, 0, 0, 1) \end{aligned} \tag{113'}$$

imposes that:

$$a(0, \mathbf{k})\, |\Psi\rangle = a(3, \mathbf{k})\, |\Psi\rangle. \tag{114}$$

The consequence of (114) is that the time-like and the longitudinal components of $a(\lambda, \mathbf{k})$ do not contribute to observables. Thus, the energy-momentum is:

$$\mathrm{P}^\nu\, |\Psi\rangle = \int d^3k k^\nu\, [a^+(1, \mathbf{k})\, a(1, \mathbf{k}) + a^+(2, \mathbf{k})\, a(2, \mathbf{k})]\, |\Psi\rangle$$

and $\mathrm{P}_0\, |\Psi\rangle$ is positive definite.

We therefore need to consider only the development:

$$\mathbf{A}(x) = \frac{1}{(2\pi)^{3/2}} \cdot \int \frac{d^3k}{\sqrt{2k^0}} \sum_{\lambda=1,2} \mathbf{e}(\lambda, \mathbf{k})\, \{a(\lambda, \mathbf{k})\, e^{-ikx} + a^+(\lambda, \mathbf{k})\, e^{ikx}\} \tag{115}$$

and the rules:

$$\begin{aligned} [a(1, \mathbf{k}), a^+(1, \mathbf{k}) &= [a(2, \mathbf{k}), a^+(2, \mathbf{k})] = \delta(\mathbf{k} - \mathbf{k}') \\ [a(2, \mathbf{k}), a(2, \mathbf{k})] &= [a(1, \mathbf{k}), a(1, \mathbf{k})] = [a(1, \mathbf{k}), a(2, \mathbf{k})] \\ &= [a(1, \mathbf{k}), a^+(2, \mathbf{k})] = 0. \end{aligned} \tag{116}$$

The number of *linearly polarized photons* is $\int a^+(\lambda, \mathbf{k})\, a(\lambda, \mathbf{k})\, d^3k$ with polarization $\lambda = 1$ or 2.

The spin angular momentum of the field (115) is, from (19), (21) and L_1 in (77):

$$\mathrm{S}^{jk} = :\int d^3x \left(\frac{\partial \mathrm{A}^j}{\partial x^0}\, \mathrm{A}^k - \mathrm{A}^j\, \frac{\partial \mathrm{A}^k}{\partial x^0} \right):$$

or:

$$S^3 = i \int d^3k \, [a^+(1, \mathbf{k}) \, a(2, \mathbf{k}) - a^+(2, \mathbf{k}) \, a(1, \mathbf{k})]. \tag{117}$$

The one-linearly-polarized photon state is not an eigenstate of S^3. You will show, with the help of (117) and (116), that:

$$\begin{aligned} S^3 \, [a^+(1, \mathbf{k}) \, |\Psi_0\rangle] &= -ia^+(2, \mathbf{k}) \, |\Psi_0\rangle \\ S^3 \, [a^+(2, \mathbf{k}) \, |\Psi_0\rangle] &= ia^+(1, \mathbf{k}) \, |\Psi_0\rangle. \end{aligned} \tag{118}$$

If you now form the linear combinations:

$$\begin{aligned} a(\mathrm{R}, \mathbf{k}) &= \frac{1}{\sqrt{2}} \, [a(1, \mathbf{k}) + ia(2, k)] \\ a(\mathrm{L}, \mathbf{k}) &= \frac{1}{\sqrt{2}} \, [a(1, k) - ia(2, k)] \end{aligned} \tag{119}$$

you will find that:

$$\begin{aligned} S^3 \, [a^+(\mathrm{R}, \mathbf{k}) \, |\Psi_0\rangle] &= a^+(\mathrm{R}, \mathbf{k}) \, |\Psi_0\rangle, \\ S^3 \, [a^+(\mathrm{L}, \mathbf{k}) \, |\Psi_0\rangle] &= -a^+(\mathrm{L}, \mathbf{k}) \, |\Psi_0\rangle. \end{aligned} \tag{120}$$

(120) suggests to call $a^+(\mathrm{R}, \mathbf{k}) \, |\Psi_0\rangle$ a one-right-circularly-polarized-photon-state, $a^+(\mathrm{L}, \mathbf{k}) \, |\Psi_0\rangle$, a one-left-circularly-polarized-photon state. $\int a^+(\mathrm{R}, \mathbf{k}) \, a(\mathrm{R}, \mathbf{k}) \, d^3k$ and $\int a^+(\mathrm{L}, \mathbf{k}) \, a(\mathrm{L}, \mathbf{k}) \, d^3k$ are the number operators of right—and left—circular photons, since (116) and (119) give the necessary communication rules for the emission and absorption operators of right and left photons:

(115) can also be written:

$$\mathbf{A}(x) = \frac{1}{(2\pi)^{3/2}} \int \frac{d^3k}{\sqrt{2k^0}} \, \{[\mathbf{e}(\mathrm{R}, \mathbf{k}) \, a(\mathrm{R}, \mathbf{k}) + \mathbf{e}(\mathrm{L}, \mathbf{k}) \, a(\mathrm{L}, \mathbf{k})] \, e^{-ikx}$$

$$+ [\mathbf{e}^*(\mathrm{R}, \mathbf{k}) \, a^+(\mathrm{R}, \mathbf{k}) + \mathbf{e}^*(\mathrm{L}, \mathbf{k}) \, a^+(\mathrm{L}, \mathbf{k})] \, e^{ikx}\} \tag{121}$$

with:

$$\begin{aligned} \mathbf{e}(\mathrm{R}, \mathbf{k}) &= \frac{1}{\sqrt{2}} \, (\mathbf{e}(1, \mathbf{k}) - i\mathbf{e}(2, \mathbf{k})) \\ \mathbf{e}(\mathrm{L}, \mathbf{k}) &= \frac{1}{\sqrt{2}} \, (\mathbf{e}(1, \mathbf{k}) + i\mathbf{e}(2, \mathbf{k})). \end{aligned} \tag{122}$$

Now, back to the parity transformation (113). First, observe that the three vectors $\mathbf{e}(1, \mathbf{k})$, $\mathbf{e}(2, \mathbf{k})$ and $\mathbf{k}$ are related by

$$\frac{\mathbf{k}}{|\mathbf{k}|} = \mathbf{e}(1, \mathbf{k}) \times \mathbf{e}(2, \mathbf{k}). \tag{123}$$

From this:

$$\frac{-\mathbf{k}}{|\mathbf{k}|} = \mathbf{e}(1, -\mathbf{k}) \times \mathbf{e}(2, -\mathbf{k}) = -\mathbf{e}(1, \mathbf{k}) \times \mathbf{e}(2, \mathbf{k}).$$

We choose:

$$\mathbf{e}(1, -\mathbf{k}) = \mathbf{e}(1, \mathbf{k}), \mathbf{e}(2, -\mathbf{k}) = -\mathbf{e}(2, \mathbf{k}), \tag{124}$$

which means that a right-handed system goes over into a left-handed system, as it must be:

$$\mathbf{e}(\mathrm{R}, -\mathbf{k}) = \mathbf{e}(\mathrm{L}, \mathbf{k}). \tag{125}$$

Now then, (113), (115) and (124) will give us:

$$\begin{aligned} \mathrm{P}a(1, \mathbf{k})\,\mathrm{P}^{-1} &= -a(1, -\mathbf{k}) \\ \mathrm{P}a(2, \mathbf{k})\,\mathrm{P}^{-1} &= +a(2, -\mathbf{k}) \\ \mathrm{P}a^{+}(1, \mathbf{k})\,\mathrm{P}^{-1} &= -a^{+}(1, -\mathbf{k}) \\ \mathrm{P}a^{+}(2, \mathbf{k})\,\mathrm{P}^{-1} &= +a^{+}(2, -\mathbf{k}). \end{aligned} \tag{126}$$

From (119), then:

$$\begin{aligned} \mathrm{P}a(\mathrm{R}, \mathbf{k})\,\mathrm{P}^{-1} &= -a(\mathrm{L}, -\mathbf{k}) \\ \mathrm{P}a(\mathrm{L}, \mathbf{k})\,\mathrm{P}^{-1} &= -a(\mathrm{R}, -\mathbf{k}) \\ \mathrm{P}a^{+}(\mathrm{R}, \mathbf{k})\,\mathrm{P}^{-1} &= -a^{+}(\mathrm{L}, -\mathbf{k}) \\ \mathrm{P}a^{+}(\mathrm{L}, \mathbf{k})\,\mathrm{P}^{-1} &= -a^{+}(\mathrm{R}, -\mathbf{k}). \end{aligned} \tag{127}$$

Thus a one-linearly-polarized-photon state is an eigenstate of **P** but not of S^3; a one-circularly-polarized-photon state is an eigenstate of S^3 but not of P.

P transforms a right-photon moving in the **k**-direction into a left-photon moving into $-\mathbf{k}$-direction. See the table below (always under the assumption $P\,|\Psi_0\rangle = |\Psi_0\rangle$):

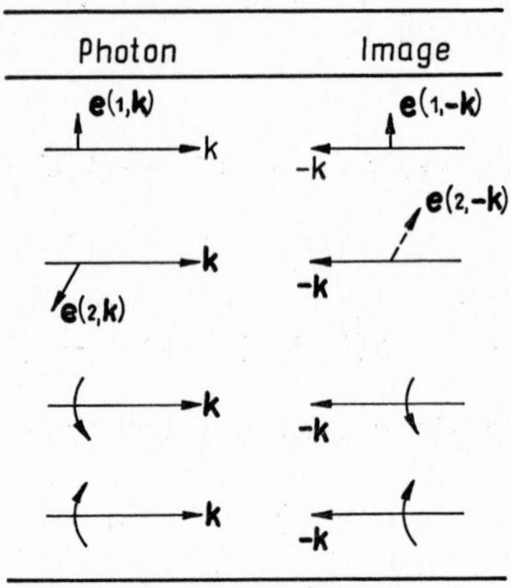

2.5 PARITY AND SPIN OF TWO-PHOTON STATES. SELECTION RULES FOR THE DECAY OF A NEUTRAL BOSON INTO TWO PHOTONS

The following are the possible state vectors of two photons with momenta **k** and $-\mathbf{k}$:

$$|\Psi(+R, -R)\rangle \equiv a^+(R, \mathbf{k})\, a^+(R, -\mathbf{k})\, |\Psi_0\rangle$$

$$|\Psi(+L, -L)\rangle \equiv a^+(L, \mathbf{k})\, a^+(L, -\mathbf{k})\, |\Psi_0\rangle$$

$$|\Psi(+R, -L)\rangle \equiv a^+(R, \mathbf{k})\, a^+(L, -\mathbf{k})\, |\Psi_0\rangle \tag{129}$$

$$|\Psi(+L, -R)\rangle \equiv a^+(L, \mathbf{k})\, a^+(R, -\mathbf{k})\, |\Psi_0\rangle$$

of which the following ones:

$$|\Psi(+R, -R)\rangle + |\Psi(+L, -L)\rangle; \quad |\Psi(+R, -R)\rangle - |\Psi(+L, -L)\rangle;$$

$$|\Psi(+R, -L)\rangle; \, |\Psi(+L, -R)\rangle$$

are the eigenstates of both P and S^3, as you will easily show. The table (129) gives the corresponding eigenvalues:

Eigenvalues and eigenstates of P and S^3

	$\lvert\Psi(+R, -L)\rangle$	$\Psi\lvert(+L, -R)\rangle$	$\lvert\Psi(+R, -R)\rangle +$ $\lvert\Psi(+L, -L)\rangle$	$\lvert\Psi(+R, -R)\rangle -$ $\lvert\Psi(+L, -L)\rangle$
P	even	even	even	odd
S^3	2	-2	0	0

(129)

If we make use of (119) we shall be able to write:

$$|\Psi(+R, -R)\rangle + |\Psi(+L, -L)\rangle$$

$$= (a^+(1, \mathbf{k})\, a^+(1, -\mathbf{k}) - a^+(2, \mathbf{k})\, a^+(2, -\mathbf{k}))\, |\Psi_0\rangle \qquad (130)$$

which shows that in this state the two photons have parallel polarization planes with equal probability for the polarization being $\lambda = 1$ and $\lambda = 2$. Also:

$$|\Psi(+R, -R)\rangle - |\Psi(+L, -L)\rangle$$

$$= -i\,(a^+(1, \mathbf{k})\, a^+(2, -\mathbf{k}) + a^+(2, \mathbf{k})\, a^+(1, -\mathbf{k}))\, |\Psi_0\rangle \qquad (131)$$

in this state, the two photons have perpendicular polarization planes. Finally:

$$|\Psi(+R, -L)\rangle = \tfrac{1}{2}\{a^+(1,\mathbf{k})\, a^+(1, -\mathbf{k}) + a^+(2,\mathbf{k})\, a^+(2, -\mathbf{k})$$

$$+\, ia^+(1,\mathbf{k})\, a^+(2, -\mathbf{k}) - ia^+(2,\mathbf{k})\, a^+(1, -\mathbf{k})\}\, |\Psi_0\rangle, \qquad (132)$$

$$|\Psi(+L, -R)\rangle = \tfrac{1}{2}\{a^+(1,\mathbf{k})\, a^+(1, -\mathbf{k}) + a^+(2,\mathbf{k})\, a^+(2, -\mathbf{k})$$

$$-\, ia^+(1,\mathbf{k})\, a^+(2, -\mathbf{k}) + ia^+(2,\mathbf{k})\, a^+(1, -\mathbf{k})\}\, |\Psi_0\rangle;$$

the two photons, in each of these states have equal chances that their polarization planes be parallel or perpendicular.

From (129) and the interpretation given in (130), (131) and (132) we are now capable to give selection rules for the decay of a neutral boson of spin 0 or 1 into two photons, which are indicated in the table (133), where $\parallel$ means that the polarization planes of the two photons are parallel, $\perp$ means that they are perpendicular to each other. The interaction responsible for the decay must be invariant under proper Poincaré transformations and under space reflections, conserving angular momentum J and parity P:

$P \setminus J$	0	1
even	$\parallel$	forbidden
odd	$\perp$	forbidden

(133)

The result is important:

1) a spin 1 neutral meson (vector or pseudovector) cannot decay into two photons;

2) positronium (bound state of an electron and a positron) in the triplet S-state, ^3S, cannot decay into two photons;

3) a scalar neutral meson can decay only into two $\parallel$ photons;

4) a pseudoscalar neutral meson decays into two $\perp$ photons;

5) positronium in the singlet S state ^1S, is odd, as will be shown later, and thus decays into two $\perp$ photons.

2.6 DETERMINATION OF THE PARITY OF BOSONS

It was emphasized, from the beginning of this chapter, that the definition of the intrinsic parity of a particle depends on the *arbitrary choice* of the value $+1$ or -1 for a number s which is indeterminate to the extent that it must satisfy the relation $s^2 = 1$ for neutral bosons and $s^*s = 1$ for charged bosons, and on the arbitrary choice $\omega_0 = 1$ in $P\,|\Psi_0\rangle = \omega_0\,|\Psi_0\rangle$.

How are we to make this choice for the particles which exist in Nature?

A well-defined procedure for bosons is the following: *first step*, choose the electric field as a polar vector, which fixes s, as was done in (113)); *and* define the vacuum state as even:

$$P\,|\Psi_0\rangle = |\Psi_0\rangle. \tag{134}$$

This determines the parity of any state which contains only photons. Next, to determine the parity of pions, look for the decay of *neutral* pions into photons. As they do decay into two photons, the π_0 cannot have spin 1. Disregarding the possibility of higher spins, as supported by other considerations, π^0 must be spinless. Then, in principle, *the second step* is to determine whether the two photons have parallel or perpendicular polarization planes.

A *pseudoscalar* π_0 leads to the latter. *The third step*, to determine the parity of the charged pions is to be guided by the charge-independence of the interaction of pions with nucleons, as described in I, 8, item 2), and to state, *as a new*, very reasonable, *assumption*, that the charged and neutral pion fields, components of a vector in the isobaric spin space, have the same parity transformation properties. This last assumption is equivalent to stating that $\psi_p\gamma^5\psi_n$ transforms in the same way as $\psi_p\gamma^5\psi_p$, $\psi_n\gamma^5\psi_n$, i.e., as a pseudoscalar, as follows from the assumed parity-invariance of the interaction lagrangian in (82).

The remaining bosons, so far known experimentally, are the K-mesons, which decay into pions, and resonances, but the determination of their parity is more involved because the corresponding coupling does not conserve parity in weak interactions.

Summing up, you will see that (104) combined with:

$$\mathrm{P}\,|\Psi_0\rangle = \omega_0\,|\Psi_0\rangle, \tag{135}$$

where $\omega_0^*\omega_0 = 1$, gives:

$$\mathrm{P}^2\mathrm{O}\,(x)\,|\Psi_0\rangle = \omega^2\mathrm{O}\,(x)\,|\Psi_0\rangle, \tag{136}$$

where

$$\omega = s\omega_0.$$

Our assumption (134) fixes $\omega_0 = 1$. The procedure described above fixes $s = 1$ for photons, $s = -1$, for pions, giving for any state vector Ψ constructed by application of Bose field operators $\mathrm{O}(x)$ to the vacuum state:

$$\mathrm{P}^2\,|\Psi\rangle = |\Psi\rangle. \tag{137}$$

It may also be appropriate to emphasize that the *third step* described above, namely, the identification of the parity of charged pions with that of neutral pions is *a new arbitrary* assumption, independent of that made for photons. This is because charged fields have an arbitrary phase factor $e^{i\alpha}$, as described in I, 4. The fact that all observables must be invariant with respect to this phase transformation leads to the conclusion that *the phases* (or *parities*) *of state vectors belonging to different charges cannot be compared.*

In fact, let Ω be such an observable. Let $|\Psi\rangle$ be an eigenstate of the charge Q with eigenvalue q:

$$\mathrm{Q}\,|\Psi\rangle = q\,|\Psi\rangle \tag{138}$$

and $|\Psi'\rangle$ an eigenstate of Q with eigenvalue q':

$$\mathrm{Q}\,|\Psi'\rangle = q'\,|\Psi'\rangle \tag{140}$$

we have:

$$\langle\Psi|\,\Omega\,|\Psi'\rangle \equiv \langle\Psi|\,e^{-iQ\alpha}\,\Omega e^{iQ\alpha}\,|\Psi'\rangle = e^{-i(q-q')\alpha}\,\langle\Psi|\,\Omega\,|\Psi'\rangle \tag{141}$$

therefore:

$$\langle\Psi|\,\Omega\,|\Psi'\rangle = 0 \tag{142}$$

unless $q = q'$.

Now, given $|\Psi\rangle$ and $|\Psi'\rangle$, form the linear combination $|\Phi\rangle = |\Psi\rangle + |\Psi'\rangle$; then:

$$|\Phi'\rangle \equiv \mathrm{P}^2\,|\Phi\rangle = \omega^2|\Psi\rangle + \omega'^2\,|\Psi'\rangle \equiv \mathrm{P}^2\,(|\Psi\rangle + |\Psi'\rangle) \tag{143}$$

where ω and ω' are phase factors. If $|\Psi\rangle$ describes neutral boson states, the assumption made in step one fixed ω. To determine ω', as a consequence of this, I could measure the expectation values of an observable Ω in the Φ'-state in the Ψ-state and in the Ψ'-state, and the transition probability between Ψ and Ψ':

$$\langle\Phi'|\,\Omega\,|\Phi'\rangle = \langle\Psi|\,\Omega\,|\Psi\rangle + \langle\Psi'|\,\Omega\,|\Psi'\rangle + (\omega^*\omega')^2\,\langle\Psi|\,\Omega\,|\Psi'\rangle$$
$$+ (\omega'^*\omega)^2\,\langle\Psi'|\,\Omega\,|\Psi\rangle. \tag{144}$$

This is, however, impossible if $q \neq q'$, because of (142). Therefore, the choice of ω' for charged systems is independent of that of ω for neutral systems.

We shall see in the next chapter that a similar selection rule operates between states with integral total angular momenta and states with half-integral total angular momenta, so that the parity of a fermion cannot be deduced from that of bosons.

CHAPTER 3

Space Reflection and Parity: Fermi Fields

3.1 PARITY TRANSFORMED OF SPINOR FIELDS

The determination of the matrix S of formula (104) when O(x) is a Dirac spinor field $\psi(x)$ is obtained by requiring that the free-field equation (10), or the free-field lagrangian L_2 in (77), be invariant under space reflection. One finds $S = \gamma^0$. Call η the phase factor s in (104):

$$P\psi(x)P^{-1} = \eta\gamma^0\psi(-\mathbf{x}, x^0) \tag{145}$$

where $\eta^*\eta = 1$. You will see that P preserves the anticommutation rules for $\psi(x)$.

One also has:

$$\begin{aligned} P\psi^+(x)P^{-1} &= \eta^*\psi^+(-\mathbf{x}, x^0)\gamma^0 \\ P\overline{\psi}(x)P^{-1} &= \eta^*\overline{\psi}(-\mathbf{x}, x^0)\gamma^0. \end{aligned} \tag{146}$$

The Fourier integral (47) and equ. (145) lead to:

$$\begin{aligned} &\int \frac{d^3p}{\sqrt{2p^0}} \sum_{r'} \{Pa(r, \mathbf{p})P^{-1}u(r, \mathbf{p})e^{-ipx} + Pb^+(r, \mathbf{p})P^{-1}v(r, \mathbf{p})e^{ipx}\} \\ &= \eta \int \frac{d^3p}{\sqrt{2p^0}} \sum_{r} \{a(r', -\mathbf{p})\gamma^0 u(r', -\mathbf{p})e^{-ipx} \\ &\quad + b^+(r', -\mathbf{p})\gamma^0 v(r', -\mathbf{p})e^{ipx}\} \end{aligned} \tag{147}$$

From (48), you will show that:

$$(\gamma^k p_k - m)\gamma^0 u(r', -\mathbf{p}) = 0, \quad (\gamma^k p_k + m)\gamma^0 v(r', -\mathbf{p}) = 0 \tag{148}$$

so that we can take:

$$\begin{aligned} u(r, \mathbf{p}) &= \varepsilon_1\gamma^0 u(r', -\mathbf{p}) \\ v(r, \mathbf{p}) &= \varepsilon_2\gamma^0 v(r', -\mathbf{p}). \end{aligned} \tag{149}$$

We fix the factors ε_1, and ε_2 in the special solutions u and v for a fermion moving along p_z, with the spin parallel or antiparallel to p_z, which are, except for a normalization coefficient:

$E > 0$	$r = \frac{\sigma_z p_z}{\lvert p_z \rvert} = 1$	$r = -1$
$u_1(r, \mathbf{p})$	1	0
$u_2(r, \mathbf{p})$	0	1
$u_3(r, \mathbf{p})$	$p_z/(E+m)$	0
$u_4(r, \mathbf{p})$	0	$-p_z/(E+m)$

(150)

$E < 0$	$r = 1$	$r = -1$
$v_1(r, \mathbf{p})$	$p_z/(\lvert E \rvert + m)$	0
$v_2(r, \mathbf{p})$	0	$-p_z/(\lvert E \rvert + m)$
$v_3(r, \mathbf{p})$	1	0
$v_4(r, \mathbf{p})$	0	1

Then, with $\gamma^0 = \begin{pmatrix} I & O \\ O & -I \end{pmatrix}$:

$$\varepsilon_1 = 1, \quad \varepsilon_2 = -1. \tag{151}$$

Thus, (147), (149) and (151) will give:

$$\begin{aligned} Pa(r, \mathbf{p})P^{-1} &= \eta a(r', -\mathbf{p}) \\ Pb^+(r, \mathbf{p})P^{-1} &= -\eta b^+(r', -\mathbf{p}) \\ Pa^+(r, \mathbf{p})P^{-1} &= \eta^* a^+(r', -\mathbf{p}) \\ Pb(r, \mathbf{p})P^{-1} &= -\eta^* b(r, -\mathbf{p}). \end{aligned} \tag{152}$$

It is clear why we used r' in the second-hand side. When you reflect $\mathbf{p}$, the helicity r changes sign, since σ does not. So when we change $\mathbf{p}$ into $-\mathbf{p}$ in the columns in (150), we have to interchange $r = 1$ and $r = -1$.

3.2 PARITY OF FERMION STATES

How are we to define the parity of a fermion?

If we adopt the convention (134), (137), namely that the repeated appica-tion of P to *any* state vector gives back this state vector:

$$P^2 |\Psi\rangle = |\Psi\rangle \tag{137}$$

then for a one-particle state Ψ_1:

$$|\Psi_1\rangle = \bar{\psi}(x) |\Psi_0\rangle$$

I obtain

$$P^2 |\Psi_1\rangle = (\eta^*)^2 |\Psi_1\rangle \tag{153}$$

since

$$P^2 |\Psi_0\rangle = |\Psi_0\rangle.$$

(137) and (153) give then:

$$\eta^2 = 1$$

and we are free to choose $\eta = +1$ or $\eta = -1$. For any of these two choices we see that a one-particle and a one-antiparticle states have *opposite relative parity*.

Yang and Tiomno have proposed some years ago, that one might also make the choice $\eta = +i$ or $\eta = -i$. Their argument is essentially the follow-ing: apply again the parity operation to (145), to obtain:

$$P^2\psi(x) P^{-2} = \eta^2\psi(x). \tag{154}$$

This corresponds to returning to the original point x in space-time and the spinor ψ, due to its double-valuedness, may change its sign; hence:

$$\eta^2 = \pm 1. \tag{155}$$

Of course, η is an arbitrary phase factor, in (145), and the choice of its value is to a certain extent arbitrary. If we adopt the convention (137), or in general, that the phase factor of the phase in:

$$P^2 |\Psi_i\rangle = \omega |\Psi_i\rangle \tag{137'}$$

is *independent* of the state vector $|\Psi_i\rangle$, then:

$$\eta^2 = 1. \tag{156}$$

Suppose that you choose to say, with Yang and Tiomno, that there may exist two families of Dirac spinor fields in Nature, one, the "real" family, for which $\eta = +1$ (or $\eta = -1$), the other, the "imaginary" family, for which $\eta = +i$ (or $\eta = -i$). Then, the convention (137′) will not hold any more, the phase ω_j in:

$$\mathrm{P}^2 \, |\Psi_j\rangle = \omega_j \, |\Psi_j\rangle \tag{157}$$

will depend on the state vector $|\Psi_j\rangle$. Thus, if you assume that for the vacuum, $\omega_0 = 1$, then

$$\mathrm{P}^2 \, |\Psi[n_r, n_i]\rangle = (-1)^{n_i} \, |\Psi[n_r, n_i']\rangle \tag{158}$$

where n_r is the number of particles of the "real" family, n_i, the number of particles of the "imaginary" family present in the state $|\Psi\rangle$.

You will note, from (152), that the intrinsic parity of a particle is opposite to that of an antiparticle of the "real" family, while the intrinsic parity of a particle is the same as that of an antiparticle of the "imaginary" family. The physically significant quantity is, however, the relative parity of a particle-antiparticle S-state and this is odd, as is clear from (152).

3.3 SUPERSELECTION RULE OF WICK–WIGHTMAN–WIGNER

After the paper of Yang and Tiomno (see bibliography), the question of the intrinsic and relative parity of bosons and fermions, was greatly clarified by an article of Wick, Wightman and Wigner. They essentially showed: (1) the parity of a neutral boson system of particles which can decay into pure photon states is well-defined if one makes a convention on the parity of a photon state; (2) the parity of charged boson states cannot be compared with that of neutral boson states, as shown in the preceding chapter, and thus needs a new, independent convention; (3) *the parity of half-integral total angular momentum states cannot be deduced from that of integral total angular momentum states* and thus, also needs another, independent, assumption. The last statement constitutes what is called the Wick–Wightman–Wigner superselection rule. In their paper, these authors gave a proof of it by using the operation of time reversal. This has the inconvenience that you may have, in principle, interactions which are not invariant under time reversal. The proof we shall give now is simple and general for all theories invariant under the proper, orthochronous Lorentz group. In such theories, all observables Ω must be relativistically covariant, i.e., tensors:

$$l_{\alpha}^{\alpha'} l_{\beta}^{\beta'} \cdots \Omega_{\alpha' \beta'} \cdots = \mathrm{U}^{-1} \Omega_{\alpha\beta} \cdots \mathrm{U} \tag{159}$$

where U is given by (26). In particular, for the element R of the group U corresponding to the rotation by the angle 2π around the z-axis, we have:

$$\Omega_{\alpha\beta} \cdots = \mathrm{R}^{-1}\Omega_{\alpha\beta} \cdots \mathrm{R} \tag{160}$$

where:

$$\mathrm{R} = e^{+i\mathrm{J}_3\varphi}, \quad \mathrm{J}_3 = \mathrm{M}^{12}, \quad \varphi = 2\pi.$$

Let Ψ be an eigenstate of J_3 with eigenvalue m:

$$\mathrm{J}_3 \,|\Psi\rangle = m\,|\Psi\rangle \tag{161}$$

and $|\Psi'\rangle$ another one with eigenvalue m':

$$\mathrm{J}_3 \,|\Psi'\rangle = m'\,|\Psi'\rangle.$$

We then have, for the transition amplitude of Ω between these two states:

$$\langle\Psi|\,\Omega\,|\Psi'\rangle \equiv \langle\Psi|\,\mathrm{R}^{-1}\Omega\mathrm{R}\,|\Psi'\rangle = e^{i(m'-m)2\pi}\,\langle\Psi|\,\Omega\,|\Psi'\rangle. \tag{162}$$

Hence:

$$\langle\Psi|\,\Omega\,|\Psi'\rangle = 0 \quad \text{unless } m-m' = \text{integral number.} \tag{163}$$

Clearly, if m is an integer and m' a half-odd integer, $\langle\Psi|\,\Omega\,|\Psi'\rangle = 0$.

Let us call $|\Psi_{\mathrm{A}}\rangle$ the Ψ'-s with m integral, $|\Psi_{\mathrm{B}}\rangle$ the Ψ'-s with m half-integral and make the combination:

$$|\Psi\rangle = |\Psi_{\mathrm{A}}\rangle + |\Psi_{\mathrm{B}}\rangle$$

Then:

$$\mathrm{P}^2\,|\Psi\rangle = \omega_{\mathrm{A}}\,|\Psi_{\mathrm{A}}\rangle + \omega_{\mathrm{B}}\,|\Psi_{\mathrm{B}}\rangle \tag{164}$$

according to (157).

Now, by (164) and (163):

$$\langle\Psi|\,\mathrm{P}^2\Omega\mathrm{P}^2\,|\Psi\rangle = \langle\Psi_{\mathrm{A}}|\,\Omega\,|\Psi_{\mathrm{A}}\rangle + \langle\Psi_{\mathrm{B}}|\,\Omega\,|\Psi_{\mathrm{B}}\rangle = \langle\Psi|\,\Omega\,|\Psi\rangle. \tag{165}$$

The term in $\omega_{\mathrm{A}}^*\omega_{\mathrm{B}}$, which would allow to deduce ω_{B} from an assignment given to ω_{A} is missing because of (163) and, thus, its determination is arbitrarily independent of ω_{A}. Both states $\mathrm{P}^2\,|\Psi\rangle$ and $|\Psi\rangle$ are indistinguishable for the computation of expectation values of observables, or in other words P^2 commutes with Ω.

3.4 FURTHER DIGRESSION ON THE "REAL"—AND "IMAGINARY"—FERMIONS

There is a subtle point at the end of the above proof. We did not make any assumption about whether P^2 commutes with all observables Ω. This was proved by (165):

$$P^{-2}\Omega P^2 = \Omega. \tag{166}$$

P being unitary. It is also a consequence of (142), (143) and (144). Therefore, as Ω is hermitian and P is unitary we have:

$$P\Omega P^{-1} = \pm\Omega.$$

This makes it impossible for us to decide physically between the assumption (137′), for which $\eta^2 = 1$, and the assumption (157), for which η^2 is arbitrary and can be taken, in particular, equal to $+1$ for some spinors and -1 for others, as indicated in (158).

As a result of (166) *you cannot have a transition between a state with an even number of "imaginary"-fermions and a state with an odd number of such particles.* If both states have the same total angular momentum and charge, as for example:

$$1 \text{ "real"-neutron} + 1 \text{ "imaginary"-neutron} \rightarrow 2 \text{ "real"-neutrons} \tag{167}$$

then (166) forbids the transition:

$$\begin{aligned}\langle\Psi_i + \Psi_f|\,\Omega\,|\Psi_i + \Psi_f\rangle &= \langle\Psi_i + \Psi_f|\,P^{-2}\Omega P^2\,|\Psi_i + \Psi_f\rangle \\ &= \langle -\Psi_i + \Psi_f|\,\Omega\,|-\Psi_i + \Psi_f\rangle\end{aligned}$$

hence:

$$\langle\Psi_f|\,\Omega\,|\Psi_i\rangle = 0 \tag{168}$$

where $|\Psi_i\rangle$ and $|\Psi_f\rangle$ are the initial and final states in (167).

The unsatisfactory circumstance in (168) is that we would like to have a quantity, like angular momentum and charge, that would not be conserved in (168). The nucleon number cannot be invoked, since real-fermions and imaginary-fermions, if both have particles and antiparticles, have a nucleon number which can be chosen to be conserved in (167).

A bose field, like the pion field, which interacts with both real and imaginary neutrons, and whose coupling is conserved under parity, cannot make the transition (167). But another field, like a vector field, whose coupling is not invariant under the parity operation—a weak coupling—can carry the transition (167).

We shall see, in chapter 5, that for neutral Majorana fermions, which belong to the imaginary family, one may have a physical justification for (168).

3.5 PARITY-TRANSFORMED OF SPINOR BILINEAR FORMS. PARITY OF NEUTRON AND PROTON

(145) and (146) justify now the names S, V, T, A, P, given to the operators in the table (76). You will easily find

	Bilinear form	Parity transformed
S	$\bar{\psi}_1(x)\,\psi_2(x)$	$\eta_1^*\eta_2\bar{\psi}_1\,(-\mathbf{x}, x^0)\,\psi_2\,(-\mathbf{x}, x^0)$
V	$\bar{\psi}_1(x)\,\gamma^0\psi_2(x)$	$\eta_1^*\eta_2\bar{\psi}_1\,(-\mathbf{x}, x^0)\,\gamma^0\psi_2\,(-\mathbf{x}, x^0)$
	$\bar{\psi}_1(x)\,\boldsymbol{\gamma}\psi_2(x)$	$-\eta_1^*\eta_2\bar{\psi}_1\,(-\mathbf{x}, x^0)\,\boldsymbol{\gamma}\psi_2\,(-\mathbf{x}, x^0)$
T	$\frac{i}{2}\,\bar{\psi}_1(x)\,[\gamma^i, \gamma^k]\,\psi_2(x)$	$\eta_1^*\eta_2\,\frac{i}{2}\,\bar{\psi}_1\,(-\mathbf{x}, x^0)\,[\gamma^i, \gamma^k]\,\psi_2\,(-\mathbf{x}, x^0)$
	$\frac{i}{2}\,\bar{\psi}_1(x)\,[\gamma^0, \gamma^k]\,\psi_2(x)$	$-\eta_1^*\eta_2\,\frac{i}{2}\,\bar{\psi}_1\,(-\mathbf{x}, x^0)\,[\gamma^0, \gamma^k]\,\psi_2\,(-\mathbf{x}, x^0)$
A	$\bar{\psi}_1(x)\,\gamma^0\gamma^5\psi_2(x)$	$-\eta_1^*\eta_2\bar{\psi}_1\,(-\mathbf{x}, x^0)\,\gamma^0\gamma^5\psi_2\,(-\mathbf{x}, x^0)$
	$\bar{\psi}_1(x)\,\boldsymbol{\gamma}\gamma^5\psi_2(x)$	$\eta_1^*\eta_2\bar{\psi}_1\,(-\mathbf{x}, x^0)\,\boldsymbol{\gamma}\gamma^5\psi_2\,(-\mathbf{x}, x^0)$
P	$i\bar{\psi}_1(x)\,\gamma^5\psi_2(x)$	$-\eta_1^*\eta_2 i\bar{\psi}_1\,(-\mathbf{x}, x^0)\,\gamma^5\psi_2\,(-\mathbf{x}, x^0)$ (169)

The geometric character shows up for $\psi_2 = \psi_1$, when the phase factors disappear.

We now see that if the constants C′ in (93) are different from zero, the Fermi coupling is not space-reflection invariant.

Consider now the coupling L' in (82). Our choice of the parity of charged bosons, made in section 2.6, imposes now, by the requirement that (82) be invariant under the parity operation, that the phases, or parities, of the neutron and proton be equal. The alternative choice would be possible as well.

CHAPTER 4

Particle–Antiparticle Conjugation

4.1 DEFINITION OF PARTICLE–ANTIPARTICLE CONJUGATION

This operation is defined as the transformation of particle states into antiparticle states.

It is frequently called *charge conjugation* by obvious reasons, but it also applies to neutral particles for which particle states are never identical to antiparticle states.

We shall abbreviate it into **C**-conjugation, where the letter **C** designates the operator in Hilbert space.

Consider (45). Then by definition:

$$\mathbf{C}a^{+}(r, \mathbf{p})\,|\Psi_0\rangle = \varepsilon^{*}b^{+}(r, \mathbf{p})\,|\Psi_0\rangle$$

$$\mathbf{C}b^{+}(r, \mathbf{p})\,|\Psi_0\rangle = \varepsilon a^{+}(r, \mathbf{p})\,|\Psi_0\rangle \tag{170}$$

where ε is an arbitrary phase factor.

If we assume, as reasonable, that:

$$\mathbf{C}\,|\Psi_0\rangle = |\Psi_0\rangle \tag{171}$$

then:

$$\mathbf{C}a^{+}(r, \mathbf{p})\,\mathbf{C}^{-1} = \varepsilon^{*}b^{+}(r, \mathbf{p}) \tag{172}$$

and:

$$\mathbf{C}^{2}a^{+}(r, \mathbf{p})\,\mathbf{C}^{-2} = a^{+}(r, \mathbf{p}) \tag{173}$$

and analogously for b^{+}. **C** conserves the commutation rules, as U and P do, and will be taken as unitary.

From (45), we see that if there exists a matrix C′ which acts on the spinor or tensor indices of O(x), such that:

$$u_{\alpha}(r, \mathbf{p}) = C'_{\alpha\beta}v^{+}_{\beta}(r, \mathbf{p}) \tag{174}$$

$$v_{\alpha}(r, \mathbf{p}) = C'_{\alpha\beta}u^{+}_{\beta}(r, \mathbf{p})$$

then:

$$\mathbf{C}O_{\alpha}(x)\,\mathbf{C}^{-1} = \varepsilon C'_{\alpha\beta}O^{+}_{\beta}(x)\,. \tag{175}$$

The reader will find easily that for a *spinless non-hermitian* field $\varphi(x)$, one has:

$$\mathbf{C}\varphi(x)\,\mathbf{C}^{-1} = \varepsilon\varphi^{+}(x)$$

$$\mathbf{C}\varphi^{+}(x)\,\mathbf{C}^{-1} = \varepsilon^{*}\varphi(x) \tag{176}$$

and that the free-field lagrangian and energy–momentum tensor are invariant under $\mathbf{C}$. The current, however, changes sign, as expected:

$$j^{\nu} = i\!:\!\left(\varphi^{+}\frac{\partial\varphi}{\partial x_{\nu}} - \frac{\partial\varphi^{+}}{\partial x_{\nu}}\varphi\right)\!: = -\mathbf{C}j^{\nu}\mathbf{C}^{-1}. \tag{177}$$

The field orbital angular momentum does not change sign.

For a *spinless hermitian field*, one has:

$$\mathbf{C}\varphi_{0}(x)\,\mathbf{C}^{-1} = \varepsilon_{0}\varphi_{0}(x) \tag{178}$$

and here $\varepsilon^{2} = 1$. ε_{0} is called the $\mathbf{C}$-conjugation parity.

4.2 EIGENSTATES OF C

We shall call *charge* of a state the number of its particles minus the number of its antiparticles. This is also the meaning of the operator Q in (55). It can be electric charge, the nucleon number, the lepton number, etc.

Now we prove that *the only possible eigenstates of* $\mathbf{C}$ *are those with total charge zero*. This is trivial. If q is the eigenvalue of Q in the state $|\Psi\rangle$

$$\mathrm{Q}\,|\Psi\rangle = q\,|\Psi\rangle \tag{179}$$

and if $|\Psi\rangle$ is an eigenstate of $\mathbf{C}$ with eigenvalue c,

$$\mathbf{C}\,|\Psi\rangle = c\,|\Psi\rangle \tag{180}$$

then:

$$\mathbf{C}\mathrm{Q}\,|\Psi\rangle = \mathbf{C}\mathrm{Q}\mathbf{C}^{-1}\mathbf{C}\,|\Psi\rangle = -\mathrm{Q}\mathbf{C}\,|\Psi\rangle = -\mathrm{Q}c\,|\Psi\rangle$$

so:

$$\mathbf{C}q\,|\Psi\rangle = qc\,|\Psi\rangle = -qc\,|\Psi\rangle$$

hence:

$$q = 0. \tag{181}$$

Now (170), (171) and (181) show that $c = \pm 1$.

The two eigenstates, $|\Psi_{+}\rangle$ and $|\Psi_{-}\rangle$, corresponding to $c = +1$ and $c = -1$ in (179), are orthogonal because $\mathbf{C}$ is unitary, and, thus any state vector $|\Phi\rangle$ can be written

$$|\Phi\rangle = \alpha\,|\Psi_+\rangle + \beta\,|\Psi_-\rangle \tag{182}$$

with the normalization:

$$\alpha^*\alpha + \beta^*\beta = 1.$$

Examples constructed with (170):

$$|\Psi_+\rangle = \frac{1}{\sqrt{2}}\,[a^+(r,\mathbf{p})\,b^+(r',\mathbf{p}') + b^+(r,\mathbf{p})\,a^+(r',\mathbf{p}')]\,|\Psi_0\rangle, \tag{183}$$

$$|\Psi_-\rangle = \frac{1}{\sqrt{2}}\,[a^+(r,\mathbf{p})\,b^+(r',\mathbf{p}) - b^+(r,\mathbf{p})\,a^+(r',\mathbf{p}')]\,|\Psi_0\rangle.$$

It is interesting to note that the relativistic invariance of the theory, which gave rise to (116), by means of the superselection rules, also leads to

$$\mathbf{C}^2\Omega\mathbf{C}^{-2} = \Omega$$

and hence to:

$$\mathbf{C}\Omega\mathbf{C}^{-1} = \pm\Omega.$$

4.3 C-CONJUGATION OF SPINOR FIELDS

The consideration of (47) and (48) and of (170), (174), (175), leads us straightforwardly to:

$$\begin{aligned}\mathbf{C}\psi(x)\,\mathbf{C}^{-1} &= \varepsilon C\bar{\psi}^{\mathrm{T}}(x)\\ u(r,\mathbf{p}) &= C\bar{v}^{\mathrm{T}}(r,\mathbf{p})\\ v(r,\mathbf{p}) &= C\bar{u}^{\mathrm{T}}(r,\mathbf{p})\end{aligned} \tag{185}$$

where T means transposition in spinor space (not in Hilbert space) and C is such that:

$$\begin{aligned}C^{-1}\gamma^k C &= -(\gamma^k)^{\mathrm{T}}\\ C^{\mathrm{T}} &= -C\end{aligned} \tag{186}$$

besides being unitary. The antisymmetric nature of C is needed for the consistency of the last two relations of (185).

From (185), it follows that:

$$\begin{aligned}\mathbf{C}\bar{\psi}^{\mathrm{T}}(x)\,\mathbf{C}^{-1} &= \varepsilon^* C^{-1}\,\psi(x)\\ \mathbf{C}\bar{\psi}(x)\,\mathbf{C}^{-1} &= -\varepsilon^*\psi^{\mathrm{T}}(x)\,C^{-1}.\end{aligned} \tag{187}$$

4.4 C-CONJUGATION OF THE SPINOR BILINEAR COVARIANTS

From (185), (186) and (187) we obtain the **C**-conjugated of the bilinear form in (76). It is important, however, to emphasize once again that the physical quantities are not those expressions in (76) but rather these expressions taken as normal products.

Thus for

$$j^\mu(x) = :\bar{\psi}(x)\,\gamma^\mu\psi\,(x):$$

we get:

$$\mathbf{C}j^\mu\,(x)\,\mathbf{C}^{-1} = -:\psi^{\mathrm{T}}\mathrm{C}^{-1}\gamma^\mu\mathrm{C}\bar{\psi}^{\mathrm{T}}\,(x): = :\psi^{\mathrm{T}}(x)\,\gamma^{\mu\mathrm{T}}\bar{\psi}^{\mathrm{T}}\,(x):$$
$$= -:\bar{\psi}(x)\,\gamma^\mu\psi\,(x):$$

In the same way one obtains the following table:

	Normal bilinear forms	C-conjugated	
S	$:\bar{\psi}_1(x)\,\psi_2(x):$	$\varepsilon_1^*\varepsilon_2:\bar{\psi}_2(x)\,\psi_1(x):$	
V	$:\bar{\psi}_1(x)\,\gamma^\mu\psi_2(x):$	$-\varepsilon_1^*\varepsilon_2:\bar{\psi}_2(x)\,\gamma^\mu\psi_1(x):$	
T	$:\frac{i}{2}\,\bar{\psi}_1(x)\,[\gamma^\mu,\gamma^\nu]\,\psi_2(x):$	$-\varepsilon_1^*\varepsilon_2:\frac{i}{2}\,\bar{\psi}_2(x)\,[\gamma^\mu,\gamma^\nu]\,\psi_1(x):$	
A	$:\bar{\psi}_1(x)\,\gamma^\mu\gamma^5\psi_2(x):$	$\varepsilon_1^*\varepsilon_2:\bar{\psi}_2(x)\,\gamma^\mu\gamma^5\psi_1(x):$	
P	$:i\bar{\psi}_1(x)\,\gamma^5\psi_2(x):$	$\varepsilon_1^*\varepsilon_2 i:\bar{\psi}_2(x)\,\gamma^5\psi_1(x):$	(188)

Note that the spin term: $\bar{\psi}\gamma_0\,[\gamma^i,\gamma^k]\,\psi$: does not change sign under **C**.

Of course the phase factors ε are restricted by requirements on the coupling with other fields. Thus, **C**-conjugation invariance of the pion nucleon coupling L' in (82) gives:

$$\varepsilon^*(p)\,\varepsilon(n)\,\varepsilon(\pi^\pm) = 1$$
$$\varepsilon(\pi^0) = 1. \qquad (189)$$

The same requirement of **C**-conjugation invariance determines uniquely the phase-factor (**C**-conjugation parity) of *neutral* (hermitian) bose fields which interact with Fermi fields. Thus, if:

$$\mathbf{C}:\bar{\psi}(x)\,\Gamma\psi\,(x):\mathrm{B}(x)\,\mathbf{C}^{-1} = :\bar{\psi}(x)\,\Gamma\psi\,(x):\mathrm{B}(x).$$

the following table results:

Neutral bose field B(x)	ε(B)
scalar	1
vector	-1
tensor	-1
pseudovector	1
pseudoscalar	1

(190)

Clearly, a superselection rule operates here: from *the assignment of the phase-factor of a neutral state you cannot deduce the phase-factor of a charged state*, and this follows from (184). Thus in (189), $\varepsilon(\pi^0) = 1$ but we are free to choose $\varepsilon(\pi^\pm)$, and once fixed the latter you are free to choose $\varepsilon(p)$ and $\varepsilon(n)$ satisfying the relation (189). In the last case, the superselection rule referred to states with integral and states with half-integral angular momenta.

The reader will now easily show the following consequences of the *assumption* of **C**-conjugate-invariant interactions:

1) the coupling of neutral scalar mesons with fermions cannot be the sum of a scalar and a vector coupling (these terms mean the coupling of S with the scalar field and of V with the 4-gradient of this field, respectively);

2) the coupling of neutral pseudovector mesons with fermions cannot be the sum of a pseudovector and a pseudotensor coupling;

3) a reaction among neutral bosons is forbidden if the number of vector couplings and tensor couplings with intermediate fermi fields, is odd. This is because, by assumption, the interaction, and hence the S-matrix, responsible for the reaction is invariant under **C**:

$$\mathbf{C}S\mathbf{C}^{-1} = S. \tag{191}$$

Then if the reaction is p initial bosons $\to$ q final bosons:

$$\begin{aligned} \Lambda &= \langle \Psi_0 | \, a_q \cdots a_1 S a_1^+ \cdots a_p^+ \, | \Psi_0 \rangle \equiv \langle \Psi_0 | \, \mathbf{C}^+ \mathbf{C} a_q \cdots a_1 S a_1 \cdots a_p^+ \mathbf{C}^+ \mathbf{C} \, | \Psi_0 \rangle \\ &= \langle \Psi_0 | \, \mathbf{C} a_q \mathbf{C}^{-1} \cdots \mathbf{C} a_1 \mathbf{C}^{-1} S \mathbf{C} a_1^+ \mathbf{C}^{-1} \cdots \mathbf{C} a_p^+ \mathbf{C}^{-1} \, | \Psi^0 \rangle. \end{aligned} \tag{192}$$

Now, each a and a^+ transforms in the negative one, if the couplings are vector and tensor, according to (190); taking also (191) into account you will see that (192) is equal to:

$$\Lambda = (-1)^{n(v)+n(t)} \Lambda.$$

Corollaries:

a) neutral vector meson → 2 photons, is absolutely forbidden (Sakata and Tanikawa);

b) neutral pseudovector meson → 3 photons, is absolutely forbidden;

c) neutral pseudovector meson → 2 photons is forbidden by (space-reflection) parity conservation;

d) transitions involving an odd number of external photon lines are absolutely forbidden;

e) neutral spinless meson → 3 photons is absolutely forbidden.

4.5 C-CONJUGATION PARITY OF PHOTON STATES

If electrodynamics is invariant under particle-antiparticle conjugation, it follows from table (190) that the **C**-conjugation parity of the electromagnetic field is -1:

$$\mathbf{C}A^{\mu}(x)\,\mathbf{C}^{-1} = -A^{\mu}(x) \tag{193}$$

which leads to:

$$\mathbf{C}a(\lambda, \mathbf{k})\,\mathbf{C}^{-1} = -a(\lambda, \mathbf{k}) \tag{194}$$

$$\mathbf{C}a^{+}(\lambda, \mathbf{k})\,\mathbf{C}^{-1} = -a^{+}(\lambda, \mathbf{k}).$$

With the choice (171), the **C**-conjugation parity of an n-photon state is $(-1)^n$:

$$\mathbf{C}a^{+}(\lambda_1, \mathbf{k}_1)\cdots a^{+}(\lambda_n, \mathbf{k}_n)\,|\Psi_0\rangle = (-1)^n\cdot a^{+}(\lambda_1, \mathbf{k}_1)\cdots a^{+}(\lambda_n, \mathbf{k}_n)\,|\Psi_0\rangle \tag{195}$$

4.6 C-CONJUGATION PARITY OF POSITRONIUM. SELECTION RULES

The state-vector of positronium in a stationary state can be developed in a perturbation series. As this is a neutral system, it may be an eigenstate of the operator **C**. This will then be true for each term of the series. To determine the C-conjugation parity, we will, therefore, need to consider only the lowest order term, which is, namely, in the center-of-momentum system (see (111)):

$$|\Psi\rangle = \sum_{r,r'} \int d^3p\cdot F(r, r', \mathbf{p})\,b^{+}(r, \mathbf{p})\,a^{+}(r', -\mathbf{p})\,|\Psi_0\rangle.$$

We then have (see (170), (171), (172)):

$$\mathbf{C}\,|\Psi\rangle = \sum_{r,r'} \int d^3p\, \mathrm{F}(r, r', \mathbf{p})\, a^+(r, \mathbf{p})\, b^+(r', -\mathbf{p})\, |\Psi_0\rangle$$

$$= -\sum_{r,r'} \int d^3p\, \mathrm{F}(r', r, -\mathbf{p})\, b^+(r, \mathbf{p})\, a^+(r', -\mathbf{p})\, |\Psi_0\rangle$$

by changing $\mathbf{p}$ into $-\mathbf{p}$, r with r', and taking into account the anti-commutativity of a and b.

Thus the definition:

$$\mathbf{C}\,|\Psi\rangle = \sum_{r,r'} \int d^3p \cdot (\mathbf{C}\mathrm{F}(r, r', \mathbf{p}))\, b^+(r, \mathbf{p})\, a^+(r', -\mathbf{p})\, |\Psi_0\rangle$$

leads to the transformation of the wave function F:

$$\mathbf{C}\mathrm{F}(r, r', \mathbf{p}) = -\mathrm{F}(r', r, -\mathbf{p}). \tag{196}$$

The effect of the **C**-conjugation is to exchange the relative momenta and the polarizations of electron and positron, with a negative sign for the resulting amplitude. As

$$r = \frac{\boldsymbol{\sigma}\cdot\mathbf{p}}{|\mathbf{p}|}, \quad r' = -\frac{\boldsymbol{\sigma}'\cdot\mathbf{p}}{|\mathbf{p}|},$$

$r \to r'$, $\mathbf{p} \to -\mathbf{p}$ lead to $\boldsymbol{\sigma} \to \boldsymbol{\sigma}'$.

Let l be the orbital angular momentum quantum number of the state. The exchange $\mathbf{p} \to -\mathbf{p}$ corresponds to an exchange of position (space-reflection of the relative coordinates). Let s be the total spin quantum number of positronium. We see that:

$$\mathrm{F}(r', r, -\mathbf{p}) = -(-1)^{l+s+1} \cdot \mathrm{F}(r, r', \mathbf{p})$$

and so:

$$\mathbf{C}\mathrm{F}(r, r', \mathbf{p}) = (-1)^{l+s} \cdot \mathrm{F}(r, r', \mathbf{p}) \tag{197}$$

$(-1)^{l+s}$ is the **C**-conjugation parity of positronium.

The following table results:

Positronium state	**C**-parity	Parity of n photons	Selection rule
^{3}S ($l = 0$, $s = 1$)	-1	$(-1)^n$	^{3}S cannot decay into even number of photons
^{1}S ($l = 0$, $s = 0$)	1	$(-1)^n$	^{1}S cannot decay into odd number of photons

4.7 FERMI INTERACTION: CONDITION ON THE COUPLING CONSTANTS BY C-CONJUGATION INVARIANCE REQUIREMENT

Straightforward application of formulas (185), (186) and (187) to the lagrangian (93) will show that if:

$$\mathbf{C}L'\mathbf{C}^{-1} = L' \tag{199}$$

then one must have:

$$\varepsilon^*(p)\, \varepsilon(n)\, \varepsilon^*(e)\, \varepsilon(\nu) = 1$$

and, moreover:

$$\mathrm{C}_i = \mathrm{C}_i^*, \quad \mathrm{C}_i' = -\mathrm{C}_i'^*, \quad i = \mathrm{S, V, T, A, P} \tag{200}$$

Experiments disprove (200), and, therefore, (199) is not true.

CHAPTER 5

Majorana Neutral Fields. Parity of Majorana Neutral Fermions

5.1 DEFINITION OF MAJORANA NEUTRAL FIELDS

We are now in condition to define a Majorana neutral field. Denote it by M(x). We shall define it as a field which is identical, except for a phase factor η, to its particle–antiparticle conjugated:

$$M(x) = \eta \mathbf{C} M(x) \mathbf{C}^{-1}. \tag{201}$$

Repetition of **C**-conjugation gives:

$$\mathbf{C} M(x) \mathbf{C}^{-1} = \eta^2 M(x) = M(x)$$

hence:

$$\eta = \pm 1. \tag{202}$$

Thus a Majorana neutral field is such that:

$$M(x) = \pm \mathbf{C} M(x) \mathbf{C}^{-1}. \tag{203}$$

The hermitian bose fields are examples of Majorana neutrals, such as the neutral pion and the electromagnetic field; neutral pions and photons are Majorana neutrals, they are identical to their antiparticles. For the electromagnetic field, the $-$ sign is taken in (203).

5.2 DIRAC AND MAJORANA FERMI FIELDS

We shall call *Dirac fermi field* a spinor field which does not satisfy (201). These are the fermions so far found in the world such as electrons, muons, protons, and the charged baryons. They may also describe neutral fermions, such as neutrons, neutrinos and the neutral strange baryons. Their antiparticles are distinct from the corresponding particles, by some physical property such as the magnetic moment, nucleon or lepton number. That their electrical charge is zero leads to state that for them $e = 0$. But for the neutral Dirac fermions, as for the charged ones, $:\bar{\psi}(x)\gamma^{\mu}\psi(x):$, as well as the other covariants of the table (76), does not vanish. This is not a satisfactory explanation and we do not know a better one.

Majorana fermi fields, i.e., spinors which satisfy (201), have not been found in nature, as yet. It may be worth while to investigate some of their properties, since we cannot exclude their existence a priori.

5.3 BILINEAR COVARIANTS OF MAJORANA FERMIONS. COMMUTATION RULES

It follows from the definition (201) and from inspection of table (188) that the V and T bilinear forms, as normal products, vanish identically for a given M(x): $:\overline{M}(x)\gamma^{\mu}M(x): = :\overline{M}(x)[\gamma^{\mu},\gamma^{\nu}]M(x): \equiv 0$.

Majorana bilinear forms	
S	$:\overline{M}(x)\,M(x):$
V	0
T	0
A	$:\overline{M}(x)\,\gamma^{\mu}\gamma^{5}M(x):$
P	$i:\overline{M}(x)\,\gamma^{5}M(x):$

(204)

Of course, this statement was based on the anticommutation properties of this field, which we shall now find. First, the spin of the field, namely $-\frac{i}{4}\overline{M}(x)\gamma^{0}[\gamma^{i},\gamma^{k}]M(x)$, is well defined.

Now, by (185) and (187), and (201), we have:

$$M(x) = \pm C\overline{M}^{T}(x)$$

$$\overline{M}(x) = \pm M^{T}(x)\,C^{-1}. \qquad (205)$$

The definition (201), (202) *must now be completed by the requirement that, in a particular representation* of the γ-matrices, M(x) *be hermitian in Hilbert space*. This is obtained by choosing, as well-known:

$$\gamma^0 = \begin{pmatrix} 0 & 0 & 0 & -i \\ 0 & 0 & i & 0 \\ 0 & -i & 0 & 0 \\ i & 0 & 0 & 0 \end{pmatrix} = -\gamma^{0*} = -\gamma^{0\mathrm{T}} \tag{206}$$

and:

$$\mathrm{C} = \pm\gamma^{0\mathrm{T}} = \mp\gamma^0. \tag{207}$$

This is the Majorana representation, in which all γ^μ's are imaginary.

We take the + sign in (205), to avoid unnecessary writing, and C in the Majorana representation is $-\gamma^0$.

The Fourier development of M(x) is:

$$\mathrm{M}(x) = \frac{1}{(2\pi)^{3/2}} \cdot \int \frac{d^3p}{\sqrt{2p^0}} \sum_r \{c\,(r, \mathbf{p})\, u\,(r, \mathbf{p})\, e^{-ipx} + c^+\,(r, \mathbf{p})\, \mathrm{C}\bar{u}^T\,(r, \mathbf{p})\, e^{ipx}\} \tag{208}$$

where $u\,(r, \mathbf{p})$ and $\bar{u}\,(r, \mathbf{p})$ are given in (48) and C, in (186).

The anticommutation rules:

$$\{c\,(r, \mathbf{p}), c^+\,(r', \mathbf{p}')\}_+ = \delta_{rr'} \cdot \delta\,(\mathbf{p} - \mathbf{p}') \tag{209}$$

$$\{c\,(r, \mathbf{p}), c\,(r', \mathbf{p}')\}_+ = \{c^+\,(r, \mathbf{p}), c^+\,(r', \mathbf{p}')\}_+ = 0$$

lead to the following ones for free fields:

$$\{\mathrm{M}_\alpha(x), \mathrm{M}_\beta(y)\} = i \cdot \mathrm{S}_{\alpha\lambda}\,(x - y) \cdot \mathrm{C}_{\lambda\beta} \tag{210}$$

where S is given in (72); and:

$$\{\mathrm{M}_\alpha(x), \overline{\mathrm{M}}_\beta(y)\}_+ = -i\mathrm{S}_{\alpha\beta}\,(x - y). \tag{211}$$

Thus, $\mathrm{M}_\alpha(x)$ and $\mathrm{M}_\beta(y)$ have an anticommutator different from zero. This shows that in the representation (206), in which M(x) is hermitian, it is *not*, however, an observable.

The anticommutation rule (210), with a right hand side different from zero is welcome indeed. Otherwise, $\mathrm{M}^2(x)$ would vanish, and in the Majorana representation, in which M(x) is hermitian, M(x) would be zero, because

$$\langle\Psi|\, \mathrm{M}^2(x)\, |\Psi\rangle = \langle\Psi|\, \mathrm{M}^+\mathrm{M}\, |\Psi\rangle.$$

The reason for the assumption of the fundamental rules (209) can be visualized in the following way. Let $\psi(x)$ be a Dirac spinor field and form the field:

$$\mathrm{M}(x) = \overset{(+)}{\psi}(x) + \overset{(-)}{\mathrm{C}\bar{\psi}^{\mathrm{T}}}(x) \tag{212}$$

where:

$$\overset{(+)}{\psi}(x) = \frac{1}{(2\pi)^{3/2}} \cdot \int \frac{d^3p}{\sqrt{2p^0}} \sum_r a\,(r, \mathbf{p})\, u\,(r, \mathbf{p})\, e^{-ipx}$$

$$\overset{(-)}{\mathrm{C}\bar{\psi}^{\mathrm{T}}}(x) = \frac{1}{(2\pi)^{3/2}} \cdot \int \frac{d^3p}{\sqrt{2p_0}} \sum_r a^+\,(r, \mathbf{p})\, \mathrm{C}\bar{u}^{\mathrm{T}}\,(r, \mathbf{p})\, e^{ipx} \tag{213}$$

are the positive-frequency part of $\psi(x)$ and the negative-frequency part of $\mathrm{C}\bar{\psi}^{\mathrm{T}}(x)$ according to (47).

From the anticommutation rules:

$$\left\{\overset{(+)}{\psi}(x), \overset{(-)}{\bar{\psi}}(y)\right\} = -i \cdot \overset{(+)}{\mathrm{S}}(x-y), \quad \left\{\overset{(-)}{\psi}(x), \overset{(+)}{\bar{\psi}}(y)\right\} = -i\overset{(-)}{\mathrm{S}}(x-y)$$

all other combinations anticommuting, you will find, by noting that:

$$\mathrm{C}^{-1}\overset{(+)}{\mathrm{S}}(x-y)\,\mathrm{C} = -\overset{(-)}{\mathrm{S}^{\mathrm{T}}}(y-x),$$

that (212) satisfies (210). Here:

$$\left(\overset{(+)}{\mathrm{S}}(x); \overset{(-)}{\mathrm{S}}(x)\right) = -i\left(\gamma^\mu \frac{\partial}{\partial x^\mu} + m\right)\left(\overset{(+)}{\Delta}(x); \overset{(-)}{\Delta}(x)\right); \quad \Delta(x) = \overset{(+)}{\Delta}(x) + \overset{(-)}{\Delta}(x).$$

5.4 POSSIBLE INTERACTIONS

The fact that $:\overline{\mathrm{M}}(x)\,\gamma^\mu\mathrm{M}\,(x):$ vanishes identically means that the charge operator $\mathrm{Q} = \int d\sigma_\mu : \overline{\mathrm{M}}(x)\,\gamma^\mu \mathrm{M}\,(x) : \equiv 0$. *A Majorana fermion is a totally neutral particle:* electric charge, nucleon number, lepton number, etc., are all zero for it. From the vanishing of

$$:\overline{\mathrm{M}}(x)\,[\gamma^\mu, \gamma^\nu]\,\mathrm{M}(x):$$

it follows also that such a particle can have no magnetic moment.

The table (204) shows that, in principle, a Majorana–Fermi field can interact only with a scalar, a pseudoscalar and a pseudovector field. It would be of interest to see whether such interactions are consistent with the anticommutation rule which follows from (210) for equal times.

If we now assume as a *general principle* that all couplings must conserve the operator Q—conservation of electric charge, of baryon number and lepton number—it is clear that in any reaction the same number of Majorana neutral fermions has to be in the initial and final states. It would thus be possible to have a heavy Majorana fermion decaying into a pair of baryons Y, $\overline{Y}$, according to:

$$M \rightarrow Y + \overline{Y} + M' \tag{214}$$

and the pair be attributed to a neutral boson. Such a decay could occur *via a weak pseudovector coupling* of the type of that which describes beta-decay. If one wishes to attribute such a Fermi weak coupling to an intermediate coupling with hypothetical heavy bosons, we see that (214) needs a neutral vector or pseudovector boson.

Thus the postulate of the existence of such a neutral heavy boson, introduced by the author recently, would allow decays (214) to be described by Feynman–Gell–Mann type of theory.

5.5 PARITY OF MAJORANA FERMIONS

From (212), we see that M(x), transforms, under P, like

$$\psi(x) + C\overline{\psi}^{T}(x).$$

By (145) and (146), we obtain:

$$PM(x)P^{-1} = \eta\gamma^{0}\overset{(+)}{\psi}(-\mathbf{x}, x^{0}) - \eta^{*}\gamma^{0}C\overset{(-)}{\overline{\psi}^{T}}(-\mathbf{x}, x^{0}) \tag{215}$$

thus in order that M(x) transform under P like a spinor we must have:

$$\eta = -\eta^{*} \tag{216}$$

which gives:

$$PM(x)P^{-1} = \eta\gamma^{0}M(-\mathbf{x}, x^{0}). \tag{217}$$

From (216), η can only be $+i$ or $-i$. Thus a Majorana–Fermi field belongs to the "imaginary" family of Yang and Tiomno.

The superselection rule forbids the transition:

2 Dirac neutral fermions → 1 Dirac neutral fermion + 1 Majorana fermion as seen in (167). We now visualize here why this must happen, if we assume conservation of lepton or baryon number.

CHAPTER 6

Time Reversal

6.1 TIME REVERSAL IN CLASSICAL PHYSICS

In classical mechanics, time reversal is the operation of inversion of the direction of motion. It changes the sign of t and of all odd functions of the velocity or momentum. The motions described by even lagrangians of the velocities (even hamiltonians of the momenta) will obey the same laws as the inverted motions. This operation is, however, not a canonical transformation. It changes the sign of the Poisson brackets of coordinates with momenta and for this reason it may be called an *anticanonical transformation.*

In classical electrodynamics, the convention that the charge density is unchanged under time reversal:

$$\varrho'(\mathbf{x}, t) = \varrho(\mathbf{x}, -t) \tag{218}$$

leads to:

$$\mathbf{j}'(\mathbf{x}, t) = -\mathbf{j}(\mathbf{x}, -t)$$

for the conservation of charge in the reversed motion.

It then follows that:

$$\begin{aligned} \mathbf{E}'(\mathbf{x}, t) &= \mathbf{E}(\mathbf{x}, -t) \\ \mathbf{H}'(\mathbf{x}, t) &= -\mathbf{H}(\mathbf{x}, -t) \\ \mathbf{A}'(\mathbf{x}, t) &= -\mathbf{A}(\mathbf{x}, -t) \\ A_0'(\mathbf{x}, t) &= A_0(\mathbf{x}, -t) \end{aligned} \tag{219}$$

for the invariance of Maxwell's equations.

In the classical electron theory, one may require that time reversal keep the energy of a free electron positive. As this is $m\dfrac{dx_0}{ds}$, where m is the rest mass and s is the proper time, this means that we should define as time reversal:

$$\mathbf{x}' = +\mathbf{x}, \quad x^{0\prime} = -x^0, \quad s' = -s. \tag{220}$$

The equations of the Lorentz electron theory are:

$$m \frac{d^2 z_\mu}{ds^2} = e\,[F_{\mu\nu}(z) + F^0_{\mu\nu}(z)] \frac{dz_\nu}{ds}; \tag{221}$$

$$\Box A^\mu(x) = e \int_{-\infty}^{\infty} \frac{dz^\mu}{ds}\, \delta\,(x - z(s))\, ds; \quad \Box A^0_\mu(x) = 0$$

$$\lim_{x^0 \to -\infty} A^\mu(x) = 0.$$

The limiting condition defines $F_{\mu\nu}(z)$ as the retarded field, $F^0_{\mu\nu}(z)$ is an external field.

Time reversal changes the boundary condition into:

$$\lim_{x^0 \to +\infty} A^\mu(x) = 0 \tag{222}$$

and thus the field goes over into the advanced one. In this case, the equations of motion are invariant under (220).

6.2 TIME REVERSAL IN NON-RELATIVISTIC QUANTUM MECHANICS

This was first investigated by Wigner, in 1932.

Consider a particle which moves with a defined momentum **p** and positive energy E. It will be described by a plane wave:

$$\psi(x) = Ae^{i(\mathbf{p}\cdot\mathbf{x} - Et)} \tag{223}$$

Our observations of the progress of this particle in time are such that the time intervals between any two of them are positive, $\Delta t > 0$. With this convention, the momentum and the energy in (223) are the eigenvalues of $-i\nabla$ and $i\frac{\partial}{\partial t}$, respectively:

$$-i\nabla\psi\,(x) = \mathbf{p}\psi\,(x)$$

$$i\frac{\partial}{\partial t}\psi(x) = E\psi\,(x), \quad E > 0. \tag{224}$$

We now want to have, under time reversal, a particle moving with momentum $-\mathbf{p}$ and positive energy E. In this new frame of reference, the time intervals between two observations are the negative of those of the original frame.

The *Schrödinger type of time reversal in Hilbert space* transforms the wave functions but not the operators. Call T this transformation. We want to have:

$$-i\nabla\,(\mathrm{T}\psi\,(x)) = -\mathbf{p}\,(\mathrm{T}\psi\,(x))$$

$$i\frac{\partial}{\partial t}(\mathrm{T}\psi\,(x)) = \mathrm{E}\,(\mathrm{T}\psi\,(x)),\quad \mathrm{E} > 0. \tag{225}$$

This will be achieved by setting:

$$\mathrm{T}\psi\,(x) = \mathrm{A}^* e^{-i(\mathbf{p}\cdot\mathbf{x}-\mathrm{E}t)} \tag{226}$$

and, in addition, having in mind that the time intervals are now negative of those of $\psi(x)$. Thus:

$$\frac{\partial}{\partial t}\mathrm{T}\psi\,(t) = -\lim_{\Delta t\to 0}\frac{\mathrm{T}\psi\,(t+\Delta t) - \mathrm{T}\psi(t)}{|\Delta t|} \tag{227}$$

if

$$\frac{\partial\psi(t)}{\partial t} = \lim_{\Delta t\to 0}\frac{\psi\,(t+\Delta t) - \psi(t)}{|\Delta t|}$$

and (225) are satisfied by (226). We see that *in Hilbert space, time reversal is here the operation of complex conjugation.*

In the *Heisenberg type of time reversal*, only the operators are transformed, not the wave functions, with the same convention on the time running backwards in the new frame of reference.

The two types of transformation must be equivalent for the observer of this frame.

How are we to express this equivalence?

We first remark that the condition (3), of the equality of the expectation values in the two types of description, is rather too strong. *What physics requires is the equality of the transition probabilities:*

$$|\langle\Psi|\,\mathrm{O}'(x)\,|\Phi\rangle|^2 = |\langle\Psi'|\,\mathrm{O}(x)\,|\Phi'\rangle|^2 \tag{228}$$

which, of course, is fulfilled by the equality of the transition amplitudes:

$$\langle\Psi|\,\mathrm{O}'(x)\,|\Phi\rangle = \langle\Psi'|\,\mathrm{O}(x)\,|\Phi'\rangle \tag{229}$$

But I could also have:

$$\langle\Psi|\,\mathrm{O}'(x)\,|\Phi\rangle = \langle\Psi'|\,\mathrm{O}(x)\,|\Phi'\rangle^* \tag{230}$$

which satisfies (228) as well.

Call K the operation of complex conjugation. This was the operation of time reversal as defined by (225) and (226):

$$T = K. \tag{231}$$

This obviously does not conserve the internal product in Hilbert space:

$$\langle K\psi | K\varphi \rangle = \langle \psi^* | \varphi^* \rangle = \langle \psi | \varphi \rangle^*. \tag{232}$$

We are thus led to adopt (230) for time reversal which shows that, in the case (231):

$$O'(x) = O^*(x), \quad \Delta t < 0. \tag{232'}$$

Thus:

$$(-i\nabla)' = K(-i\nabla)K = (-i\nabla)^* = i\nabla$$

$$\left(i\frac{\partial}{\partial t}\right)' = K\left(i\frac{\partial}{\partial t}\right)K = \left(i\frac{\partial}{\partial t}\right)^* = -i\frac{\partial}{\partial t}. \tag{233}$$

These must be applied, in the Heisenberg picture, to the unchanged ψ, (223), with the convention $\Delta t < 0$.

Usually, one takes this convention into account by stating that the transformation is complex conjugation in Hilbert space, and $t \to -t$ (as was analogously employed in the space-reflection and corresponding parity transformation):

$$T\psi(x) = \psi^*(\mathbf{x}, -t)$$

$$T^{-1}(-i\nabla)T = i\nabla \tag{234}$$

$$T^{-1}\left(i\frac{\partial}{\partial t}\right)T = i\frac{\partial}{\partial t}.$$

The hamiltonian $H(\mathbf{x}, -i\nabla)$ will be invariant if it is an even function of the momentum operator, so that $H^* = H$.

6.3 TIME REVERSAL OF THE PAULI SPINOR FUNCTION

The non-relativistic spin $\frac{1}{2}$-particle is described, in the c-number theory, by the 2-component Pauli spinor.

Let $H(x)$ be an external magnetic field. The hamiltonian:

$$H = -\frac{1}{2m}\nabla^2 + V(r) + \frac{e}{2m}(\boldsymbol{\sigma}\cdot H) \tag{235}$$

will transform, under (232′), into:

$$H^* = -\frac{1}{2m}\nabla^2 + V(r) - \frac{e}{2m}(\boldsymbol{\sigma}^* \cdot H) \tag{236}$$

because, according to (219), the convention $\Delta t < 0$ in the transformed frame entails $\mathbf{H} \rightarrow -\mathbf{H}$. For H, (235), to be invariant under time reversal, one needs, besides complex conjugation, a unitary operator such that:

$$U^{-1}H^*U = H$$

i.e.,

$$U^{-1}\boldsymbol{\sigma}^*U = -\boldsymbol{\sigma}; \quad U\mathbf{x} = \mathbf{x}U, \quad U\mathbf{p} = \mathbf{p}U.$$

In the usual representation of the Pauli matrices:

$$\sigma_x = \begin{pmatrix} 0 & 1 \\ 1 & 0 \end{pmatrix}, \quad \sigma_y = \begin{pmatrix} 0 & -i \\ i & 0 \end{pmatrix}, \quad \sigma_z = \begin{pmatrix} 1 & 0 \\ 0 & -1 \end{pmatrix}$$

we see that:

$$U = \sigma_y.$$

Therefore, now T is given by:

$$T = \sigma_y K. \tag{237}$$

6.4 SQUARE OF TIME REVERSAL ON THE SCHRÖDINGER AND THE PAULI WAVE FUNCTIONS

Of course, both (231) and (237) could have an arbitrary phase factor ε:

$$\varepsilon\varepsilon^* = 1.$$

If:

$$T = \varepsilon K$$

we get:

$$T^2 = \varepsilon K \varepsilon K = \varepsilon\varepsilon^* = I. \tag{238}$$

If

$$T = \varepsilon\sigma_y K$$

then:

$$T^2 = \varepsilon\sigma_y K\, \varepsilon\sigma_y K = \sigma_y\sigma_y^* = -I. \tag{239}$$

It will be shown later that $T^2 = I$ for all states with an integral total angular momentum and $T^2 = -I$ for all states with a half-integral total angular momentum.

6.5 TIME REVERSAL IS AN ANTIUNITARY OPERATION

A linear and unitary operation O defined on a space of functions ψ is one which satisfies the two conditions:

$$\mathrm{O}\,(\alpha_1\psi_1 + \alpha_2\psi_2) = \alpha_1\mathrm{O}\psi_1 + \alpha_2\mathrm{O}\psi_2 \tag{240}$$

$$(\mathrm{O}\psi_1, \mathrm{O}\psi_2) = (\psi_1, \psi_2) \tag{241}$$

where α_1 and α_2 are complex numbers.

The operation of complex conjugation K:

$$\mathrm{K}\psi = \psi^*$$

does not fulfill (240) nor (241). It satisfies the following two relations:

$$\mathrm{K}\,(\alpha_1\psi_1 + \alpha_2\psi_2) = \alpha_1^*\mathrm{K}\psi_1 + \alpha_2^*\mathrm{K}\psi_2 \tag{242}$$

called *antilinearity* condition, and:

$$(\mathrm{K}\psi_1, \mathrm{K}\psi_2) = (\psi_1, \psi_2)^* \tag{232}$$

called antiunitarity relation.

The complex conjugate of an operator Ω is $\Omega^* = \mathrm{K}\Omega\mathrm{K}$.

Every antilinear and antiunitary operator T (simply called antiunitary) is the product of a unitary operator U by K:

$$\mathrm{T} = \mathrm{UK} \tag{243}$$

(this U will not be confused with U(L) in (26)).

This follows from the fact that $\mathrm{K}^2 = \mathrm{I}$ and that T and K satisfy both (232) and (242).

Time reversal is in general given by (243). Example: (237).

From (243) it follows that $\mathrm{T}^2 = \pm\mathrm{I}$. Indeed, T^2 must be $c\mathrm{I}$, where c is a complex number.

Now:

$$\mathrm{T}^2 = \mathrm{UKUK} = \mathrm{UU}^* = \mathrm{U}(\mathrm{U}^{-1})^{\mathrm{T}} = c\mathrm{I}$$

hence:

$$\mathrm{U} = c\mathrm{U}^{\mathrm{T}}$$

$$\mathrm{U}^{\mathrm{T}} = c^2\mathrm{U}^{\mathrm{T}}, \quad c = \pm 1. \tag{244}$$

$c = +1$ for integral angular momentum states, while $c = -1$ for half-integral angular momentum states, as will be proved later.

The antiunitarity of T shows itself also in the fact that it does not conserve commutation rules which have imaginary commutators. Thus, as $x' = T^{-1}xT = x$, $p' = T^{-1}pT = -p$, we see that:

$$[x, p] = i$$

goes over into:

$$[x', p'] = -i. \tag{245}$$

Also:

$$[J_1, J_2] = iJ_3$$

goes over into:

$$[J'_1, J'_2] = -iJ'_3$$

where

$$J'_i = TJ_iT^{-1} = -J_i.$$

6.6 TIME REVERSAL OF DIRAC'S SPINOR FUNCTIONS

We are still in the c-number theory, where $\psi(x)$ is a Dirac spinor function, not quantized. Consider the Dirac equation of a particle in a classical electromagnetic field:

$$\left(\gamma^k\left(i\frac{\partial}{\partial x^k} - eA_k\right) - m\right)\psi(x) = 0 \tag{246}$$

$$\left(\gamma^{kT}\left(i\frac{\partial}{\partial x^k} + eA_k\right) + m\right)\overline{\psi}^T(x) = 0 \tag{247}$$

where T as an upper index means transposition in spinor space.

We want the time reversed spinor $\psi'(x')$ to satisfy Dirac's equation in the time reversed frame:

$$\left(\gamma^k\left(i\frac{\partial}{\partial x^{k'}} - eA'_k\right) - m\right)\psi'(x') = 0 \tag{248}$$

$$\left(\gamma^{kT}\left(i\frac{\partial}{\partial x^{k'}} + eA'_k\right) + m\right)\overline{\psi}^{T'}(x') = 0 \tag{249}$$

where:

$$\mathbf{x}' = \mathbf{x}, \quad x^{0\prime} = -x^0. \tag{250}$$

Take (250) and (219) into (248). This will be identical to (247) if:

$$\psi'(x') = \varepsilon B\overline{\psi}^T(x) \tag{251}$$

where ε is an arbitrary phase factor and:

$$B^{-1}\gamma^0 B = (\gamma^0)^T \tag{252}$$

$$B^{-1}\boldsymbol{\gamma} B = -(\boldsymbol{\gamma})^T$$

or:

$$B^{-1}\gamma^\mu B = (\gamma^0\gamma^\mu\gamma^0)^T. \tag{253}$$

From this, you prove, by taking the hermitian conjugate, that B is unitary:

$$B^+ = B^{-1}.$$

Now, take the transpose of (251), you will show that $B^T B^{-1}$ commutes with γ^μ, hence by Schur's lemma:

$$B^T = kB, \quad k \text{ being a number.} \tag{254}$$

Now:

$$B = kB^T = k^2 B$$

$$k = \pm 1.$$

Which of these two values must we take? By means of (253), you will see that the following relations hold for the 16 matrices:

$$\begin{aligned}
B^T &= kB \\
(\gamma^0 B)^T &= k\,(\gamma^0 B) \\
(\boldsymbol{\gamma} B)^T &= -k\,(\boldsymbol{\gamma} B) \\
(\gamma^0 \boldsymbol{\gamma} B)^T &= k\,(\gamma^0 \boldsymbol{\gamma} B) \\
(\gamma^i\gamma^j B)^T &= -k\,(\gamma^i\gamma^j B), \quad i \neq j, \quad i, j = 1, 2, 3; \\
(\gamma^0\gamma^5 B)^T &= k\,(\gamma^0\gamma^5 B) \\
(\gamma^i\gamma^5 B)^T &= -k\,(\gamma^i\gamma^5 B), \quad i = 1, 2, 3; \\
(\gamma^5 B)^T &= -k\,(\gamma^5 B).
\end{aligned}$$

Only for $k = -1$, do we get 6 antisymmetric matrices and 10 symmetric matrices, as it must be.

So:

$$B^T = -B. \tag{255}$$

A choice of B is:

$$B = \gamma^0\gamma^5 C \tag{255'}$$

where C is defined by (186).

If one now takes (250) and (219) into (249), one finds:

$$\bar{\psi}'(x') = \eta\psi^{\mathrm{T}}(x)\,\mathrm{B}^{-1} \tag{256}$$

η is another arbitrary phase factor, which will be fixed in terms of ε of (251) by a condition on the transformation of $\bar{\psi}(x)\,\psi(x)$.

6.7 TIME REVERSAL IN QUANTUM FIELD THEORY

In the c-number theory, the hermitian conjugate $\psi^{+}(x)$ of a spinor means this operation in spin space. When $\psi(x)$ is an operator, we have used, in (47), $\psi^{+}(x)$ to designate the hermitian conjugate of ψ in both spin and Hilbert space.

Thus formulae (251) and (256) are well expressed in the c-number theory. In quantum field theory, however, we must take complex conjugation in Hilbert space. Denote by a *superscript* H the *operation of transposition in Hilbert space*. If we still keep the convention (47), that ψ^{+} is the hermitian conjugate of ψ in Hilbert space, I must rewrite the transformed of ψ and $\bar{\psi}$, as operators, as follows:

$$\begin{aligned} \mathrm{T}^{-1}\psi(x)\,\mathrm{T} &= \varepsilon\mathrm{B}\bar{\psi}^{\mathrm{TH}}(\mathbf{x}, -x^{0}) \\ \mathrm{T}^{-1}\bar{\psi}(x)\,\mathrm{T} &= \eta\psi^{\mathrm{TH}}(\mathbf{x}, -x^{0})\,\mathrm{B}^{-1}. \end{aligned} \tag{257}$$

Let us give the general definition of time reversal in quantum field theory. We assume (230) and (243):

$$\begin{aligned} \langle\Psi|\,\mathrm{O}'(x)\,|\Phi\rangle &= \langle\Psi'|\,\mathrm{O}(x)\,|\Phi'\rangle^{*} \\ |\Psi'\rangle &= \mathrm{T}\,|\Psi\rangle = \mathrm{UK}\,|\Psi\rangle \\ \mathrm{UU}^{+} &= \mathrm{U}^{+}\mathrm{U} = \mathrm{I} \end{aligned} \tag{258}$$

we obtain:

$$\langle\Psi|\,\mathrm{O}'(x)\,|\Phi\rangle = \langle\Psi|\,\mathrm{KU}^{-1}\mathrm{O}(x)\,\mathrm{UK}\,|\Phi\rangle^{*}$$

thus:

$$\mathrm{O}'(x) = (\mathrm{U}^{-1}\mathrm{O}(x)\,\mathrm{U})^{*}. \tag{259}$$

Call:

$$\mathrm{V} = \mathrm{U}^{*}, \quad \mathrm{VV}^{+} = \mathrm{V}^{+}\mathrm{V} = \mathrm{I}.$$

Then:

$$\mathrm{O}'(x) = \mathrm{V}^{-1}\mathrm{O}^{*}(x)\,\mathrm{V}. \tag{260}$$

Therefore, if a physicist calculates a transition amplitude of an operator $O(x)$ between two states, the initial $|\Phi\rangle$ and the final $|\Psi\rangle$, $\langle\Psi| O(x) \Phi\rangle$, the physicist of the time reversed frame of reference will compute the transition amplitude $\langle\Psi| O'(x) |\Phi\rangle$ with $O'(x)$ given by (260). The transformed of the former amplitude is thus:

$$\langle\Psi| V^{-1}O^{*} (x) V |\Phi\rangle. \tag{262}$$

This may also be written:

$$\langle\Psi| V^{-1}O^{+H} (x) V |\Phi\rangle = \langle\Phi^{*}| U^{+}O^{+} (x) U |\Psi^{*}\rangle. \tag{263}$$

The last expression gives rise to a rule: *to transform a transition amplitude* $\langle\Psi| O(x) |\Phi\rangle$ *between an initial and a final state, calculate the amplitude of* $O^{+}(x)$ *between the transformed of the original final state as the new initial state and the transformed of the original initial state as the new final state:*

$$\langle\Psi| O(x) |\Phi\rangle \rightarrow \langle\Phi| KU^{+}O^{+} (x) UK |\Psi\rangle \tag{263'}$$

where O^{+} is hermitian conjugate of O in Hilbert space.

Consider the product of two or more operators $O_1(x_1) O_2(x_2)$. We have:

$$[O_1(x_1) O_2(x_2)]' = V^{-1}O_1^{*}(x_1) O_2^{*}(x_2) V \tag{264}$$

I can also write:

$$\begin{aligned}\langle\Psi| V^{-1}O_1^{*} (x_1) O_2^{*}(x_2) V |\Phi\rangle &= \langle\Psi| V^{-1}O^{+H} (x_1) O_2^{+H}(x_2) V |\Phi\rangle \\ &= \langle\Psi| V^{-1} (O_2^{+}(x_2) O_1^{+}(x_1))^{H} V |\Phi\rangle \\ &= \langle\Phi | KU^{+}O_2^{+} (x_2) O_1^{+}(x_1) UK |\Psi\rangle. \end{aligned} \tag{265}$$

We thus see that the transformed amplitude of:

$$\langle\Psi| O_1(x_1) O_2(x_2) |\Phi\rangle \text{ is } \langle\Phi| T^{-1}O_2^{+} (x_2) O_1^{+}(x_1) T |\Psi\rangle. \tag{266}$$

Hence the following rule, due to Schwinger and Pauli (*Niels Bohr and the development of Physics*, McGraw-Hill Book Company (1955), page 30): the transition amplitudes of the product of *hermitian* operators transform, under time reversal, into the transition amplitudes of the inverted product of these operators. This is the case of all observables. Another way of saying is: if you read the matrix element of the product of hermitian operators from left to right, read the time reverted matrix element from right to left.

6.8 TIME REVERSAL TRANSFORMATION OF THE SPINOR BILINEAR FORMS

This is now obvious with the result (266). The operators O(x) are now the spinors which transform as given in (257). O′(x), in (260), is now of the form BO*(x) where B acts on the spinor indices. $\bar{O}'(x)$ will be of the form $\bar{O}^{TH}(x)\,B^{-1}$. Thus, instead of (266), we will now have:

$$\langle\Psi|\bar{O}_1(x_1)\,\Gamma O_2(x_2)|\Phi\rangle \to \langle\Phi|\,T^{-1}\bar{O}_2(x_2)\,(B^{-1}\Gamma B)^T\,O_1(x_1)\,T\,|\Psi\rangle \quad (267)$$

where Γ is one of the 16γ-matrices, and B satisfies (253). The transposition H in Hilbert space to arrive at (266) will entail the transition T in spinor space. If we call $\bar{O}_2(x_2)\,(B^{-1}\Gamma B)^T O_1(x_1)$ the transformed of $\bar{O}_1(x_1)\,\Gamma O_2(x_2)$, we shall obtain the following table:

	Bilinear form $\bar{O}_1(x_1)\,\Gamma O_2(x_2)$	Time reverted $\bar{O}_2(x_2)\,(B^{-1}\gamma^\mu B)^T\,O_1(x_1)$ in (267) $(\varepsilon_1^*\varepsilon_2)^{-1}$
S	$\bar{\psi}_1(x_1)\,\psi_2(x_2)$	$\bar{\psi}_2(x_2)\,\psi_1(x_1)$
V	$\bar{\psi}_1(x_1)\,\gamma^\mu\psi_2(x_2)$	$\bar{\psi}_2(x_2)\,\gamma^0\gamma^\mu\gamma^0\psi_1(x_1)$
T	$\frac{i}{2}\,\bar{\psi}_1(x_1)\,[\gamma^\mu,\gamma^\nu]\,\psi_2(x_2)$	$-\frac{i}{2}\,\bar{\psi}_2(x_2)\,\gamma^0\,[\gamma^\mu,\gamma^\nu]\,\gamma^0\psi_1(x_1)$
A	$\bar{\psi}_1(x_1)\,\gamma^\mu\gamma^5\psi_2(x_2)$	$\bar{\psi}_2(x_2)\,\gamma^0\gamma^\mu\gamma^0\gamma^5\psi_1(x_1)$
P	$i\,\bar{\psi}_1(x_1)\,\gamma^5\psi_2(x_2)$	$-\,i\,\bar{\psi}_2(x_2)\,\gamma^5\psi_1(x_1)\,\varepsilon$ (268)

In (257), we take $\eta = \varepsilon^*$ so as to have no phase factor in the transformed of bilinear forms of one spinor field.

6.9 CONDITIONS FOR INVARIANCE OF THE FERMI BETA-DECAY INTERACTION UNDER TIME REVERSAL

These follow immediately from the transformations (268) and the requirement of invariance of L given by (93).

One obtains:

$$\varepsilon^*(p)\,\varepsilon(n)\,\varepsilon^*(e)\,\varepsilon(\nu) = 1$$

and

$$C_i = C_i^*, \quad C_i' = C_i'^*, \quad i = S, V, T, A, P. \quad (269)$$

Time reversal invariance of the β-decay processes imposes that the coupling constants in (93) be real.

6.10 TIME REVERSAL OF EMISSION AND ABSORPTION OPERATORS OF FERMIONS

We leave it to the reader to verify, with the help of (257), (47), (255′) and the tables (150), that:

$$\begin{aligned} T^{-1}a(r, \mathbf{p})\,T &= \varepsilon a^*(r, -\mathbf{p}) \\ T^{-1}b^+(r, \mathbf{p})\,T &= -\varepsilon b^{\mathrm{H}}(r, -\mathbf{p}) \\ T^{-1}a^+(r, \mathbf{p})\,T &= \varepsilon^* a^{\mathrm{H}}(r, -\mathbf{p}) \\ T^{-1}b(r, \mathbf{p})\,T &= -\varepsilon^* b^*(r, -\mathbf{p}). \end{aligned} \tag{270}$$

If we employ the rule (263), we will *have hermitian conjugation instead of complex conjugation, and no transposition H, in the second-hand side of* (270). In this case, one has to keep in mind that *initial and final states are switched in the same operation.*

6.11 TIME REVERSAL OF BOSE FIELDS

It will be left to the reader to find the transformations for spinless and vector fields.

For the electromagnetic field, one imposes that (260) lead to transformations like the classical ones (219).

One then obtains for photons

$$\begin{aligned} T^{-1}a(\mathrm{R}, \mathbf{k})\,T &= -a^*(\mathrm{R}, -\mathbf{k}) \\ T^{-1}a(\mathrm{L}, \mathbf{k})\,T &= -a^*(\mathrm{L}, -\mathbf{k}) \\ T^{-1}a^+(\mathrm{R}, \mathbf{k})\,T &= -a^{\mathrm{H}}(\mathrm{R}, -\mathbf{k}) \\ T^{-1}a^+(\mathrm{L}, \mathbf{k})\,T &= -a^{\mathrm{H}}(\mathrm{L}, -\mathbf{k}). \end{aligned} \tag{271}$$

Thus time reversal keeps the polarization of photons (as expected because both spin and momentum change sign):

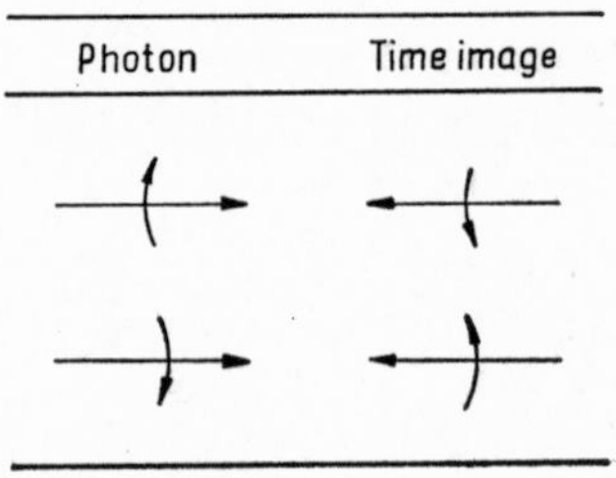

(272)

6.12 RECIPROCAL THEOREM. PRINCIPLE OF DETAILED BALANCING

Consider a reaction which transforms a state with n particles with momenta $\mathbf{p}_1, \ldots, \mathbf{p}_n$, at $t = -\infty$, into a state with k particles with momenta $\mathbf{p}'_1, \ldots, \mathbf{p}'_k$. Let $r_1, \ldots, r_n$ and $r'_1, \ldots, r'_k$ be the corresponding polarization variables.

The transition amplitude of the reaction is:

$$\Lambda = \langle \Psi_0 | \, b\,(r'_k, \mathbf{p}'_k) \cdots a\,(r'_1, \mathbf{p}'_1)\, \mathrm{S} a^+\,(r_1, \mathbf{p}_1) \cdots b^+\,(r_n, \mathbf{p}_n \,|\Psi_0\rangle$$

where S is the S-matrix.

Invariance of the transition amplitude under time eversalr gives:

$$\Lambda = \varepsilon\, \langle \Psi_0 | \, b\,(r_n, -\mathbf{p}_n) \cdots a\,(r_1, -\mathbf{p}_1)\, \mathrm{S} a^+\,(r'_1, -\mathbf{p}'_1) \cdots b^+\,(r'_k, -\mathbf{p}'_k)\, |\Psi_0\rangle$$

where ε is a phase factor.

Thus such an invariance entails the equality of the following reaction probabilities:

$$|\langle \Psi\,[r'_1, \mathbf{p}'_1, \ldots, r'_k, \mathbf{p}'_k]|\, \mathrm{S}\, |\Psi\,[r_1, \mathbf{p}_1, \ldots, r_n, \mathbf{p}_n]\rangle|^2$$

$$= |\langle \Psi\,[r_1, -\mathbf{p}_1, \ldots, r_n, -\mathbf{p}_n]|\, \mathrm{S}\, |\Psi\,[r'_1, -\mathbf{p}'_1, \ldots, r'_k, -\mathbf{p}'_k]\rangle|^2. \quad (273)$$

The principle of detailed balancing is a particular case of the last relation by omitting the negative sign of the momenta. It is valid only if the interaction is invariant under both parity transformation and time reversal, TP.

6.13 THE SQUARE OF TIME REVERSAL IS -1 FOR HALF-INTEGRAL ANGULAR MOMENTUM STATE

It follows from (255) and (257) that for a spinor field $\psi(x)$:

$$\mathrm{T}^{-2} \psi\,(x)\, \mathrm{T}^2 = -\psi(x). \quad (274)$$

Therefore for any state $|\Psi\rangle$ with an odd number of fermions:

$$|\Psi_\mathrm{B}\rangle = \psi_1(x_1) \cdots \psi_n(x_n)\, |\Psi_0\rangle$$

one obtains:

$$\mathrm{T}^{-2}\, |\Psi_\mathrm{B}\rangle = -\psi_1(x_1) \cdots \psi_n(x_n)\, \mathrm{T}^{-2}\, |\Psi_0\rangle$$

The natural assumption:

$$T^{-2}\,|\Psi_0\rangle = |\Psi_0\rangle$$

gives:

$$T^{-2}\,|\Psi_B\rangle = -|\Psi_B\rangle$$

or:

$$T^2\,|\Psi_B\rangle = -|\Psi_B\rangle. \qquad (275)$$

For integral angular momentum states:

$$T^2\,|\Psi_A\rangle = |\Psi_A\rangle. \qquad (276)$$

CHAPTER 7

Strong Reflection

7.1 DEFINITION OF STRONG REFLECTION

It is the change of particles into antiparticles accompanied of space reflection and time reversal.

The classical formulare (218), (219) are here replaced by:

$$\begin{aligned} \varrho'(x) &= -\varrho(-x) \\ j'(x) &= -j(-x) \\ \mathbf{E}'(x) &= \mathbf{E}(-x) \\ \mathbf{H}'(x) &= \mathbf{H}(-x) \\ \mathbf{A}^{\mu'}(x) &= -\mathbf{A}^{\mu}(-x). \end{aligned} \tag{278}$$

In non-relativistic quantum mechanics, one can easily derive the transformation S in the space of wave functions which corresponds to a strong reflection. (223) is transformed, in the Schrödinger type of strong reflection, into:

$$\mathrm{S}\psi\,(x) = \psi^*(x) \tag{279}$$

with the convention that the intervals Δt, Δx_i, $i = 1, 2, 3$ *in the measurements in state* $\mathrm{S}\psi$ *are the negative of those in the measurements in state* ψ. One requires that momenta and energies do not change, which is satisfied by this transformation.

The abbreviated form, analogous to (234) is:

$$\begin{aligned} \mathrm{S}\psi\,(x) &= \psi^*(-x) \\ \mathrm{S}^{-1}(-i\nabla)\,\mathrm{S} &= -i\nabla \\ \mathrm{S}^{-1}\left(i\frac{\partial}{\partial t}\right)\mathrm{S} &= i\frac{\partial}{\partial t} \end{aligned} \tag{280}$$

As the charge now changes its sign, the transformation

$$S = \sigma_y K \tag{281}$$

represents also strong reflection for the invariance of (235).

7.2 STRONG REFLECTION OF FIELD OPERATORS

S may be represented by the product CPT. Now CP is a unitary operator because C and P are unitary. T, we saw, is the product of a unitary operator U by complex conjugation. Thus we may also write

$$S = WK \tag{282}$$

where W is unitary.

Thus, extending the definitions (258) for S, (282), in place of T, we obtain:

$$O'(x) = (W^{-1} O\,(x)\,W)^*. \tag{283}$$

Now the operator W, which is essentially CP, changes O(x) into its hermitian conjugate in Hilbert space. Thus, we obtain:

$$O'(x) = M^{-1} O^{H}\,(x)\,M \tag{284}$$

where H is the transposed in Hilbert space and M is a unitary operator.

A transition amplitude $\langle \Psi|\,O(x)\,|\Phi\rangle$ transforms, under strong reflection, into:

$$\langle \Psi|\,O(x)\,|\Phi\rangle \rightarrow \langle \Psi|\,M^{-1} O^{H}\,(x)\,M\,|\Phi\rangle = \langle \Phi^*|\,(M^*)^{-1} O(x)\,M^*\,|\Psi^*\rangle \tag{285}$$

The rule is: *if you interchange initial and final states, the transformed amplitude will be that of* O(x) *with the new states.*

Also:

$$\langle \Psi|\,O_1(x_1)\,O_2(x_2)\,|\Phi\rangle \rightarrow \langle \Phi^*|\,(M^*)^{-1}\,O_2(x_2)\,O_1(x_1)\,M^*\,|\Psi^*\rangle \tag{286}$$

with an obvious rule (compare with that following (266)).

The following are the transformation laws under strong reflection:

Operator F(x) in $\langle\Psi\vert F(x)\vert\Phi\rangle$	Strong reflected F′(x) in $\langle\Phi^*\vert(M^*)^{-1} F'(x) M^*\vert\Psi^*\rangle$	
Spinor $\psi(x)$	$\varepsilon\gamma^5\psi(-x)$	
Adjoint spinor $\overline{\psi}(x)$	$-\varepsilon^*\overline{\psi}(-x)\gamma^5$	
Fermi annihilation operator $a(r, \mathbf{p})$	$\varepsilon b^+(r, \mathbf{p})$	
Creation operator $a^+(r, \mathbf{p})$	$\varepsilon^* b(r, \mathbf{p})$	
$b(r, \mathbf{p})$	$\varepsilon^* a^+(r, \mathbf{p})$	(287)
$b^+(r, \mathbf{p})$	$\varepsilon a(r, \mathbf{p})$	
$:\overline{\psi}_1(x_1)\psi_2(x_2):$	$:\overline{\psi}_1(-x_1)\psi_2(-x_2):$	
$:\overline{\psi}_1(x_1)\gamma^\mu\psi_2(x_2):$	$-:\overline{\psi}_1(-x_1)\gamma^\mu\psi_2(-x_2):$	
$:\overline{\psi}_1(x_1)\frac{i}{2}[\gamma^\mu,\gamma^\nu]\psi_2(x_2):$	$:\overline{\psi}_1(-x_1)\frac{i}{2}[\gamma^\mu,\gamma^\nu]\psi_2(-x_2):$	
$:\overline{\psi}_1(x_1)\gamma^\mu\gamma^5\psi_2(x_2):$	$-:\overline{\psi}_1(-x_1)\gamma^\mu\gamma^5\psi_2(-x_2):$	
$i:\overline{\psi}_1(x_1)\gamma^5\psi_2(x_2):$	$i:\overline{\psi}_1(-x_1)\gamma^5\psi_2(-x_2):$	

You will note that for the bilinear spinor forms the transformation laws given above refer to the normal products. *They do not hold for the forms as ordinary products.* Thus:

$$\overline{\psi}_2(x_2)\gamma^5\overline{\psi}_1(x_1) \to -\psi_1^{\mathrm{T}}(-x_1)\gamma^{5\mathrm{T}}\overline{\psi}_2^{\mathrm{T}}(-x_2). \tag{288}$$

You must also note that from the table one should not conclude that $a^+a \to bb^+$. The true transformation is, without changing initial into final state, $a^+a \to b^{\mathrm{H}}b^{+\mathrm{H}} = (b^+b)^{\mathrm{H}}$. When you now switch initial and final states, as assumed in the above table, then: $a^+a \to b^+b$.

This shows that the energy-momentum vector P^μ and the momentum tensor $M^{\mu\nu}$ transform as:

$$\mathrm{P}^\mu \to \mathrm{P}^\mu \tag{289}$$

$$M^{\mu\nu} \to -M^{\mu\nu}$$

as it is intuitive from the representation of S as CPT.

7.3 THE *CPT*-THEOREM

We note that, according to the table (287), scalars and pseudoscalars transform in the same way under strong reflection. This is true for vectors and pseudovectors.

As a result, *all interaction lagrangians* which were previously constructed by the condition of *hermitianity and invariance under the proper and orthochronous Lorentz group and as normal products* are *automatically invariant under strong reflection*.

This statement, in its general form, constitutes the so-called *CPT-theorem*. You may check this with the Fermi interaction lagrangian, by means of the table (287).

First we observe that, according to (286), the expectation value of normal products of operators transforms in the following way:

$$\langle \Psi | : O_1(x)\, O_2(x) : | \Phi \rangle \to \pm \varepsilon^2 \langle \Phi^* | \, (M^*)^{-1} : O_1(-x)\, O_2(-x) : M^* \, | \Psi^* \rangle \tag{290}$$

where we have allowed for a phase factor in (282). The $\pm$ sign comes from the Bose or Dirac statistics which the O's obey:

This factor ε appears in the spinor transformation given in table (287). Pauli has restricted its value by imposing that the reality conditions which the dotted and undotted spinors obey, be preserved under strong reflection. Let ψ^{λ} and $\psi_{\dot{\lambda}}$ be the two 2-component spinors which form ψ:

$$\psi = \begin{pmatrix} \psi^{\lambda} \\ \psi_{\dot{\lambda}} \end{pmatrix} \tag{291}$$

and choose γ^5 diagonal

$$\gamma^5 = \begin{pmatrix} I & 0 \\ 0 & -I \end{pmatrix}. \tag{292}$$

Then as $\psi \to \varepsilon \gamma^5 \psi$ under strong reflection, we have:

$$\psi^{\lambda} \to \varepsilon \psi^{\lambda}; \quad \psi_{\dot{\lambda}} \to -\varepsilon \psi_{\dot{\lambda}} \tag{293}$$

hence:

$$\psi_{\dot{\lambda}} \to -\varepsilon \psi_{\dot{\lambda}}.$$

Now $\psi_{\dot{\lambda}}$ transforms like $(\psi^{\lambda})^*$ so that we can set:

$$\psi_{\dot{\lambda}} = (\psi^{\lambda})^*. \tag{294}$$

If we require that this reality condition be preserved under strong reflection we must have:

$$-\varepsilon\psi^{\dot{\lambda}} = (\varepsilon\psi^{\lambda})^*$$

hence:

$$\varepsilon^* = -\varepsilon. \tag{295}$$

Thus, under this additional requirement, ε must be $+i$ or $-i$.

Any tensor or spinor entity can be expressed as a function $u(k, l)$ of two indices k, l and

$$u(k, l) \text{ is a spinor, if } 2(k + l) = \text{odd integral number,}$$
$$u(k, l) \text{ is a tensor, if } 2(k + l) = \text{even integral.} \tag{296}$$

For ψ one has for ψ^{λ} and $\psi^{\dot{\lambda}}$, $u(\frac{1}{2}, 0)$ and $u(0, \frac{1}{2})$ respectively, and the transformation laws under strong reflection, (293), can be written:

$$u(\tfrac{1}{2}, 0) \rightarrow \varepsilon u(\tfrac{1}{2}, 0)$$
$$u(0, \tfrac{1}{2}) \rightarrow \varepsilon^* u(0, \tfrac{1}{2}) = -\varepsilon u(0, \tfrac{1}{2}) \tag{297}$$

These relations will be generalized for tensors and higher order spinors as follows:

$$u(k, l) \rightarrow -\varepsilon(-1)^{2k}\, u(k, l) \text{ for } 2(k + l) = \text{odd, i.e., for } \textit{spinors;}$$
$$u(k, l) \rightarrow (-1)^{2k}\, u(k, l) \quad \text{for } 2(k + l) = \text{even, i.e., for } \textit{tensors,} \tag{298}$$

under strong reflections. The first relation (298) is a generalization of (297) for higher order spinors. The second relation (298) is a generalization of the transformation of the coordinates, to higher order tensors. Of course, in the transformed frame one has to take into account the convention: Δx^{μ} are the negative of the Δx^{μ} in the original frame.

Now according to (298), a product of n *spinors* transforms as:

$$u(k_1, l_1) \cdots u(k_n, l_n) \rightarrow (-\varepsilon)^n (-1)^{2(k_1 + \cdots + k_n)}\, u(k_n, l_n) \cdots u(k_1, l_1) \tag{299}$$

while a product of n *tensors*, according to (298), transforms as follows:

$$u(k_1, l_1) \cdots u(k_n, l_n) \rightarrow (-1)^{2(k_1 + \cdots + k_n)}\, u(k_n, l_n) \cdots u(k_1, l_1) \tag{300}$$

for $2(k_1 + \cdots + k_n) = \text{even}$.

We see that (300) transforms like a tensor, if:

$$u(k_1, l_1) \cdots u(k_n, l_n) = u(k_n, l_n) \cdots u(k_1, l_1).$$

Consider, however, (299). If n is even, the product (299) is a tensor, hence one must have

$$(-\varepsilon)^n (-1)^{2(k_1+\cdots+k_n)} = (-1)^{2(k_1+\cdots+k_n)} \text{ for } n \text{ } even,$$

and

$$u(k_1, l_1) \cdots u(k_n, l_n) = u(k_n, l_n) \cdots u(k_1, l_1). \qquad (301)$$

If n is odd, (299) is another spinor, if the u's commute; hence, according to (299) and (298), one must have:

$$(-\varepsilon)^n (-1)^{2(k_1+\cdots+k_n)} = -\varepsilon(-1)^{2(k_1+\cdots+k_n)} \text{ for } n \text{ } odd. \qquad (302)$$

There is, therefore, in the c-number theory, an extra factor in (299), which is, according to (301) and (302):

$$(-\varepsilon)^n, \quad \text{for } n \text{ even;}$$

$$(-\varepsilon)^{n-1}, \text{ for } n \text{ odd}$$

or:

$$(-\varepsilon)^{2\nu}, \text{ for } n = 2\nu, \ \nu \text{ integer;}$$

$$(-\varepsilon)^{2\nu}, \text{ for } n = 2\nu + 1, \ \nu \text{ integer.}$$

So the extra-factor is: $(-\varepsilon)^{2\nu} = (-1)^{n(n-1)/2}$.

This extra-factor, which is needed for the consistency of the transformation formulae (298), is obtained automatically in the transformation of *normal products* of operators. Indeed, from (299) we get:

$$:u(k_1, l_1) \cdots u(k_n, l_n): \to (-\varepsilon)^n (-1)^{2(k_1+\cdots+k_n)} :u(k_n, l_n) \cdots u(k_1, l_1):$$
$$= (-1)^{n(n-1)/2} (-\varepsilon)^n (-1)^{2(k_1+\cdots+k_n)} :u(k_1, l_1) \cdots u(k_n, l_n):$$

where $(-1)^{n(n-1)/2}$ came from the anticommutation of spinors, which has to be taken into account in the normal product.

The general formula of transformation of a normal product of field operators which may contain $j\gamma^\mu$ matrices (*distinct* from γ^5) is:

$$\langle\Psi| :O_1(x_1)\Gamma_1 \cdots \Gamma_j O_n(x_n): |\Phi\rangle \to (-1)^j (-1)^{n(n-1)/2} (-\varepsilon)^n$$
$$\times (-1)^{2(k_1+\cdots+k_n)} \langle\Phi^*| (M^*)^{-1} :O_1(x_1)\Gamma_1 \cdots \Gamma_j O_n(x_n): M^* |\Psi^*\rangle. \qquad (304)$$

The coefficient $(-1)^j$ came from the anticommutation of Γ's with γ^5, needed because of the transformation formulae for ψ in (287).

Now, the *CPT*-theorem is actually proved by considering that for all observables $\Omega_{\alpha\beta\gamma\ldots}(x)$, the proper and orthochronous Lorentz group transforms them into:

$$U^{-1}(L)\,\Omega_{\alpha\beta\ldots}(x)\,U(L) = l_{\alpha}^{\alpha'} l_{\beta\ldots}^{\beta'}\,\Omega_{\alpha'\beta'}\,(L^{-1}x). \tag{305}$$

Thus the *transformation* (304) *is preserved under the proper orthochronous Lorentz transformation.*

7.4 THEOREM

Corresponding groups of particles and antiparticles have the same energy spectrum.

Consider n free particles. We have:

$$H_0 = \sum a^+ (r, \mathbf{p})\, a\,(r, \mathbf{p})\, p^0$$

and their energy is:

$$\langle\Psi|\, H_0\, |\Psi\rangle = E_0.$$

Under strong reflection

$$\langle\Psi|\, a^+ (r, \mathbf{p})\, a\,(r, \mathbf{p})\, |\Psi\rangle = \langle\Psi|\, b^+ (r, \mathbf{p})\, b\,(r, \mathbf{p})\, |\Psi\rangle$$

hence:

$$E_0\ (\text{particles}) = E_0\ (\text{antiparticles}).$$

The contributions from the interaction energy are also invariant. A particular case is, thus: the masses of particles and antiparticles are equal.

Appendices to Part Two

I THE ANGULAR MOMENTUM OF A SPINOR FIELD

The lagrangian, the energy–momentum vector and the angular momentum tensor must be hermitian operators. Formulae such as (18) and (21), taken as normal products, must be completed with terms in the hermitian conjugate of the field so that this reality requirement is fulfilled.

The lagrangian of a free spinor field may be taken as L_2 in (77) when the hermitianity condition is not invoked. The hermitian lagrangian of this field is the following:

$$L = :\frac{i}{2}\left(\bar{\psi}\gamma^{\mu}\frac{\partial\psi}{\partial x^{\mu}} - \frac{\partial\bar{\psi}}{\partial x^{\mu}}\gamma^{\mu}\psi\right) - m\bar{\psi}\psi:$$

The energy–momentum tensor is:

$$\mathrm{T}^{\nu}_{\beta} = :\frac{i}{2}g^{\alpha\nu}\left(\bar{\psi}\gamma_{\beta}\frac{\partial\psi}{\partial x^{\alpha}} - \frac{\partial\bar{\psi}}{\partial x^{\alpha}}\gamma_{\beta}\psi\right)$$

$$+\,\delta^{\nu}_{\beta}\left(-\frac{i}{2}\left(\bar{\psi}\gamma^{\mu}\frac{\partial\psi}{\partial x^{\mu}} - \frac{\partial\bar{\psi}}{\partial x^{\mu}}\gamma^{\mu}\psi\right) + m\bar{\psi}\psi\right):$$

and the angular momentum tensor density:

$$M^{\lambda}_{\alpha\beta} = \mathrm{T}^{\lambda}_{\alpha}x_{\beta} - \mathrm{T}^{\lambda}_{\beta}x_{\alpha} + \mathrm{S}^{\lambda}_{\alpha\beta}$$

where:

$$\mathrm{S}^{\lambda}_{\alpha\beta} = -\frac{i}{8}:(\bar{\psi}\gamma^{\lambda}[\gamma_{\alpha},\gamma_{\beta}]\psi + \bar{\psi}[\gamma_{\alpha},\gamma_{\beta}]\gamma^{\lambda}\psi):$$

Thus the angular momentum of the spinor field has the form:

$$M^{\mu\nu} = \int d\sigma_{\lambda}M^{\lambda;\mu\nu}.$$

We see that $M^{\mu\nu}$ is hermitian. The spin part is:

$$\mathrm{S}^{\mu\nu} = -\frac{i}{8}\int d^3x:(\psi^{+}[\gamma^{\mu},\gamma^{\nu}]\psi + \psi^{+}\gamma^{0}[\gamma^{\mu},\gamma^{\nu}]\gamma^{0}\psi):$$

which shows that $S^{0k} = 0$. The reader may verify that this is consistent with (38) by making use of the relation:

$$\gamma^\lambda [P_\lambda, \psi(x)] = -m\psi(x)$$

for a free field, which follows from (37).

II ON THE PROOF OF THE SUPERSELECTION RULE

In the left-hand side of formula (159), we could allow for a phase factor ε. Due to the fact that U is unitary and the observables Ω are hermitian, this factor can only be 1 or -1. The choice $\varepsilon = 1$ is imposed by the assumption that observables transform like (proper) tensors under the inhomogeneous proper orthochronous Lorentz group.

When, however, U acts on a state vector there is an indeterminate phase factor ω. Allowing for such factor, the relations (162) are replaced by:

$$\langle\Psi|\, \omega^* R^{-1} \Omega \omega' R\, |\Psi'\rangle = \omega^*\omega' \langle\Psi|\, \Omega\, |\Psi'\rangle$$

in virtue of (160); and:

$$\langle\Psi|\, \omega^* R^{-1} \Omega \omega' R\, |\Psi'\rangle = \omega^*\omega' e^{2\pi i(m-m')} \langle\Psi|\, \Omega\, |\Psi'\rangle$$

due to (161). Hence:

$$\langle\Psi|\, \Omega\, |\Psi'\rangle = 0$$

if $m' - m =$ half-integer, independently of ω and ω'.

References

Many papers have been written on the subject and most are quoted in 5, 6, and 7 below:

1. E. P. WIGNER, *Group theory and its Application to Quantum Mechanics*, Academic Press (1959).
2. W. E. THIRRING, *Principles of Quantum Electrodynamics*. Academic Press (1958).
3. C. N. YANG and J. TIOMNO, *Phys. Rev.* **79**, 495 (1950).
4. G. C. WICK, A. S. WIGHTMAN and E. P. WIGNER, *Phys. Rev.* **88**, 101 (1952).
5. G. C. WICK, *Ann. Rev. Nucl. Sci.* **8**, 1 (1958).
6. E. CORINALDESI, *Nucl. Phys.* **7**, 305 (1958).
7. W. PAULI, *Niels Bohr and the Development of Physics*, McGraw-Hill (1955).
8. J. TIOMNO, *Princeton thesis* (1950).
9. J. LEITE LOPES, *An. Acad. Brasil. Ci.*, **23**, 39 (1951).
10. J. LEITE LOPES, *Nucl. Phys.* **8**, 243 (1958).
11. M. LEVY, *Dispersion Relations and Invariance Principles*, Latin American School of Physics, Mexico (1959).
12. J.D. BJORKEN and S.D. DRELL, *Relativistic Quantum Fields*, McGraw-Hill (1965).
13. H. BURKHARDT, *Dispersion Relation Dynamics*, Wiley-Interscience (1969).
14. S. DE BENEDETTI, *Nuclear Interactions*, Wiley (1964).
15. M. GELL-MANN and Y. NE'EMAN, *The Eightfold Way*, W.A. Benjamin (1965).
16. L.B. OKUN, *Weak Interactions of Elementary Particles*, Pergamon Press (1966).
17. L. WOLFENSTEIN, Weak Interaction Theory, *Proc. Heidelberg Elem. Particles Intern. Conference*, North-Holland (1968).
18. F.E. LOW. *Symmetries and Elementary Particles*, Gordon and Breach (1967).
19. S.L. ADLER and R.F. DASHEN, *Current Algebras*, W.A. Benjamin (1968).
20. J.J. SAKURAI, *Currents and Mesons*, University of Chicago Press (1968).